1.99
B # 45

The Pattern Recognition Theory Of Humour

First published 2008
Pyrrhic House
Cumbria, UK

ISBN 978-0-9559365-0-0

www.pyrrhichouse.co.uk

The Pattern Recognition Theory Of Humour

Alastair Clarke

𝐴Pyrrhic House

"An evolutionary and cognitive explanation of humour via: a statement of principles; the mechanism of humour; the nature of contentless patterns; the apprehension of entities and their surprising recognition in pattern form; patterns, pattern definition and the criterion of repetition; assisted recognition; pattern fidelity; complexity in cross-media and compound patterns; techniques of pattern application and combination; illustrations in two models of humour; the ontogenic mechanism; conscious analogues to humour; evolutionary benefits and function; data transferral and the external signal; a consideration of phylogeny and recapitulation; a revision of prior assumptions; laughter in peer groups; socialization and the acquisition of the altruistic impulse; implications of this theory in the zoological debate; applications in artificial intelligence and contributions to the analysis of dysfunction in neurology and psychology."

Contents

Function

Implications

Appendices

Foreword

I expect this theory to draw substantial criticism, in no small part because I have pronounced it global in nature. A proportion of the criticism, I would like to think, I have predicted and pre-empted, but I am sure I shall soon be more than adequately furnished with that which I have not.

In addition to the points I specify in *Premisses And Principles*, there are broader social and academic reasons for the length of time it's taken us to sort out what's going on in humour. Its apparently bewildering diversity led many people to presume it was a philosophical or a literary issue (a notion that still persists to some not insignificant degree in certain quarters) to be debated without a verifiable solution, which in turn has led many individuals of a scientific frame of mind to consider it unworthy of their attention. Further, the subject has something of a bad image, since the association of humour with levity has done it no favours with serious-minded intellectuals. This theory, I hope, will start to set that right, since the mechanism underlying humour is of fundamental importance to human cognition, and its effects during phylogenic evolution and infantile development are serious matters indeed. I am reminded of the words of my flustered computer science teacher, who, faced daily with an unruly and hysterical class, would take to shouting *Now stop laughing and get on with your work. It's time to stop laughing!*

I don't expect to receive any philosophical accolades for this work. I have only ever intended it to be judged on the correctness of the solution rather than the quality or complexity of the debate. Neither do I expect to win any awards for my observation of protocol.

I first started work on my *pattern recognition theory* in 1995, returning to it in 2001 before abandoning it again until recent media coverage of related fields led to a resurgence of my interest in the matter. It has long been my intention to produce a valid theory of humour that did not stipulate the content of the stimulus, to produce an explanation that applied to any instance of any person finding anything funny at any point, whether I, or anyone else in the world, agree or not. It is at times counter-intuitive, and although not complex at its simpler levels, requires some strictness of thought during application. I have made this explanation as lucid and as readily accessible as possible, but the apparent simplicity of the mechanism described herein should not mislead the reader into presuming that all instances of humour will now become instantly transparent, and nor, conversely, should failure to apply the theory in an effective manner cast doubt on its value. Comprehension is one thing; application is another. As yet there have been no instances of humour, whether stock types or individual examples in any medium, that I have been unable to explain according to the mechanism described in these pages.

The full-length book, *Humour*, is more popular in tone, and features extensive illustration and extrapolation not possible in this publication. It also includes the results of my field research not included here.

While working on this theory I have been struck by quite how much we have overlooked in humour, and quite how much our brains have been telling us about its nature while we've been grubbing about for an explanation: in our verbal expressions about the subject; in our reactions to it; in the ways we have developed its formats and applications. Our minds have always known the answer.

What I've written here necessarily disagrees with much that has been written elsewhere, but I would suggest to you that what has been produced elsewhere has failed to provide a satisfactory explanation of humour, and I would hope that anyone who would acknowledge the truth of such a statement would also take the time to consider what I propose herein.

Alastair Clarke
Spring 2008

Principles

Investment

Humour is important. To deny this, to overlook the resources that have been invested in it, would be to deny the basic pressures of economy at work in evolution. Even a cursory examination of its nature reveals the extent to which we have underestimated the contribution humour must have made to the success of the species. As a positive appraisal we might remark on how elating we find it, how explosive and engaging it is, but these aspects become all the more intriguing when we consider how expensive, interruptive and diverting it can be.

Neither should we fail to be struck by its universality. The famous instance of humour in David Attenborough's 1971 documentary *A Blank On The Map*, in which Laurie Bragg, the Australian explorer and cartographer, is laughed at by a member of the Biami tribe for getting the name of a local river amusingly incorrect, was interpreted correctly at the time as a sign of the underlying similarity of all human beings. The Biami had, up until that point, been an *uncontacted tribe*, yet the moment of laughter when they realize his mistake is identical in cause and expression to millions occurring globally every day, and immediately the Biami appear not so much similar to their westernized interlocutors as identical: in motivation, in comprehension, and in temperament. Its existence everywhere in such identical formats, in tribes that have never encountered the outside world, confirms that humour is far more than a learnt cultural pastime, that it is instead a fundamental mechanism shared by the whole species, serving a valued and important function for every individual.

Humankind has, in turn, awarded it immense importance socially. Its centrality to our culture, to our individual identities and our choice of companions, is continually reflected and reinforced by its existence as one of the most popular and dominant forms of entertainment in which humans partake. Such power has it expressed to us individually that it is considered one of the defining elements of our personalities, and our *sense* of humour can make or break our ties with another human being. From the class clown to joke books and stand-up comedians, from situation comedies and films to absurdist images, amusing songs, quips and one-liners, banter and wit, satire and mimicry, we are surrounded by humour.

Terminology

Common terms used within this theory are defined as followed:

The *humorous response* refers to the internal and external reactions evoked by humour, including both the egocentric neurophysiological reward and the laughter produced as its overt signal. The internal reaction may include a combination of increased arousal and neuronal activity, the release of rewards in the form of endorphins, hormones and neurotransmitters, instant responses in the autonomic nervous system and alterations in the levels of stress hormones.

The *stimulus* is the item or event, as currently recognized, in which the individual finds something amusing. The *source*, however, is the precise trigger to the humorous mechanism. There may be many sources of humour within one stimulus for any individual, and, indeed, their potential incidence is infinite.

The *element, term, sequence* and *pattern* are the units of pattern formation as illustrated in Figure 4.

Resolution refers not to the meaningful absorption of information as used by some psychological theories but to the point at which multiple terms cease to be a sequence and become a fully-fledged pattern, or at which a pattern to which we had not previously been alerted becomes suddenly apparent to us. Beyond this point, any further addition of terms will consist purely of repetition.

Cessation refers to the point at which an established pattern ceases to repeat. It may be applied retrospectively to a previously unacknowledged pattern.

Meta-pattern refers simply to a pattern which is itself constituted of smaller or more frequent patterns.

The *individual* is the person exposed to the stimulus who may or may not identify sources of humour within it.

The *transmitter* is the person who communicates patterns as they have recognized them.

Principles And Premisses

Four major problems have retarded our comprehension of humour and the research undertaken relating to it in recent years: a failure to define the difference between the overt signal of laughter and the humorous response as a whole, which involves effects that are both visible and external and invisible and internal; a failure to recognize the humorous response as a reward and the significance of this on an evolutionary basis; the concentration of interest on laughter as opposed to humour; and the presumption, still, that certain things are inherently funny, or that an objective *quality* of humour can be assessed.

Out of these assumptions has developed a very uneven interpretation of humour. By examining the (undeniably useful) application of the by-product researchers have attempted to define the function of the product itself; worse, by doing so they have attempted to discern the nature of its mechanism. The work conducted on laughter, although laudable, has fed back into the system and distorted our comprehension of humour. This has led to a tendency to presume that the function of humour is, in fact, solely to produce its overt signal in the form of laughter.

★

15

There are eleven major premisses and principles underpinning this theory.

First, humour can exist in any situation, and no stipulations of content can be made. Global interpretations based on content have long failed to attain cogency unless restricted to explaining only a fraction of humorous instances. The person who laughs when no one else does, the ability of two people to laugh at the same stimulus for different reasons, the simple fact that not all individuals find the same things funny (sometimes to the point of confrontation or censorship), the necessarily cultural basis to interpretations of content yet the universal existence of humour and the ability for the same stimulus to be found amusing to varying degrees throughout an individual's life, all prevent us from identifying content as the basis of humour's mechanism. Even some psychological mini-theories, while claiming to have escaped the confines of content-stipulation, imply the necessary existence of certain sociological conditions or events for humour to exist, such as *disparagement* (Zillmann, 1983), which presumes the presence of social formats or their substitutes in humour. Overlooking instances of humour contrary to stipulations is simply overlooking evidence, and renders any such theory redundant. Humour exists wherever anybody finds anything funny, and that is all.

Second, if no stipulations of content can be made, the basis of humour must exist in some other element that is present in every instance of its occurrence. Further, if an instance of humour can arise in any information the individual can absorb, the mechanism of humorous functionality must have the potential to exist in, or be set in motion by, any information or the manner in which any information is processed.

Third, the process of humour is unconscious, else we should all be able to explain its mechanism by simple analysis of what we think before we laugh.

Fourth, the individual often experiences a humorous response, a reward, for apparently doing nothing, by simply reacting to an external stimulus[1]. Consequently, the process being rewarded must be internal, and as a reward it must be presented for achievement. Since the reward is an emotion in itself, and emotions are not achievements, it can be

---

[1] This apparent dislocation of activity and reward has led to the misconception that the humorous response is primarily a form of social appreciation.

reasonably concluded that the reward is not for the attainment of an emotional state, and, indeed, no specific emotion exists in all instances prior to the response. Information is received, and the individual is suddenly rewarded. We therefore consider that the reward exists for some activity the individual performs on that information, which must necessarily constitute a cognitive process of some form.

Fifth, rewards exist for beneficial achievement, to encourage activity and motivate behaviour. Since they are expensive in terms of resources, and since the greater the reward the more it will dominate our preoccupations, with some degree of approximation we can assume that the greater the reward, the more important the activity being rewarded. In humour, therefore, the cognitive process being rewarded must be significant but universally applicable. Further, it is unlikely that such a rewarding biological phenomenon is not adaptive per se, and even if it were, we would still wish to identify the mechanism by which it works.

Sixth, once content has been removed, we retain only the residual impression of the structures underpinning it. Humour exits in many forms, across many media, occurring, in fact, in any format that can be communicated to the individual. The possibility of its occurrence in any medium means that our identification of those structures underpinning its mechanism can not be media-specific. Not only are they without content, but they are without media, since they must be apprehensible in visuals, linguistics, actions, processes, sounds or any other form of communication, and they must, by implication, be identical in format in each.

Seventh, the mechanism by which such information is found amusing is identical in any format or medium. Denying this proposition would leave us in a difficult position, since we should have to say that different types of humour exist in different media, each with their different mechanisms and, most likely, different functions. Visual humour would function by the recognition of information relevant only to that medium in a unique manner unrelated to linguistic or physical humour and would serve a purpose different from any other. This is an untenable proposition on an evolutionary level for many reasons, failing to explain as it does how or why each new medium of appreciation evolved. There is also little reason to believe that the human mind is so inefficient as to process basic information in entirely different ways dependent upon its medium of communication.

Eighth, psychometric testing in the field has been misleading, since *comprehension* of humour is not possible without a working knowledge of its mechanism.

Ninth, previous *incongruity* theories, while approaching elements of the correct mechanism, are inadequate as an explanation of humour, not least due to the difficulties of defining the central term. The objections are well known. Much of what is humorous is founded in complicity and repetition as opposed to incongruity, as in many instances of *translational mapping* in different media. Also, the inability to explain why some forms of incongruity should lead to humour and others not, especially since much that is incongruous is negative for the individual and leads to entirely different emotions, led to the proposed introduction of a stipulation that the condition of the humour should be playful or inconsequential, since incongruity in itself is an insufficient condition of humour. The new conditions, however, by resurrecting unnecessary stipulations of content, fail to explain many instances of humour.

Further, there is little or no evolutionary basis for such theories. The *resolution* involved is seen as the absorption of incongruous information in a meaningful way, yet there can be little reason to do so if the information is inconsequential, and even less reason to reward the individual for doing so. Even if we are to believe that such activity encourages adaptability, it ignores the fact that adaptation is only ever *necessary* due to adverse, consequential circumstances, and is certainly not restricted to positive, inconsequential ones. Again, it also fails to explain why the individual should wish to advertise such attention to inconsequentials in the form of the overt signal, or why the process of meaningful resolution, if it really is meaningful, should be unconscious.

Tenth, information regarding any subject from any source has a common feature only in non-specific units of data, of terms and entities arranged in different formations. We may, within the presentation of such data, recognize patterns.

Finally, we accept that laughter, as a proportion of the humorous response and its overt signal, must perform some function of communication, but that this function is not the reason for the existence of humour.

★

We can now say that humour is a process of cognition, and that the associated humorous response of neurophysiological chemical release is a reward for the achievement of that cognition, simultaneously communicated via the overt signal of laughter.

Mechanism

Pattern Recognition

The apprehension of entities and their recognition in pattern form will be returned to repeatedly in this book. The mechanism of pattern recognition is the process by which entities are first apprehended and then reassessed in adapted circumstances. The identity of a unit is first perceived, followed by comprehension of that unit in an adapted state. By this process of recognition we learn to apply similar patterns to different terms, and to identify similar terms in different patterns. The recognition of patterns is, therefore, a facet of cognitive economy.

It is fundamental to this theory that it is the recognition of the pattern that evokes a humorous response, not the content, although content is still necessary for us to be able to decipher the pattern beneath it. Without content there can be no pattern, yet once the content exists, the pattern is the level at which humour operates, at which it exercises its process of recognition, and for which it delivers its rewards.

Patterns, Pattern Definition And The Criterion Of Repetition

In order to understand humour we must take a moment to understand the process of pattern recognition behind it, and to do so we will need to identify exactly what constitutes a pattern and its constituent terms.

A pattern exists in a sequence of terms in which we discern some level of repetition, some criterion of internal connection. It should be noted, however, that there are different forms of repetition, and, as we'll see later, the level at which repetition operates might not be the simple unit, but the criterion for alteration between one unit and the next.

Consider the following sequence:

Figure 1

Analysed one way there is no pattern here, since most of the individual units (terms) are different in the sequence. Even the repetition of the first term as the last is insufficient to produce a pattern, since the sequence, when apprehended as a whole, features no repetition. However, we could develop this into a pattern by adjusting our identification of the initial term, reducing the sequence to four elements instead of five, and then employing the fifth element to initiate an instance of replication of the first four elements, whereby we recognize a simple two-term repetition thus:

Figure 2

Or, indeed, the potential for a central point of symmetry halfway through an element might lead us to reconfigure the pattern thus:

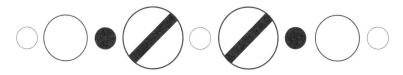

Figure 3

To clarify our analysis here it will be appropriate to refer to the unit of repetition as a *term*, the collection of terms as a *sequence* if we fail to discern repetition, the collection of terms as a *pattern* if we discern repetition, and any smaller entities exhibited in the composition of a unit as *elements*:

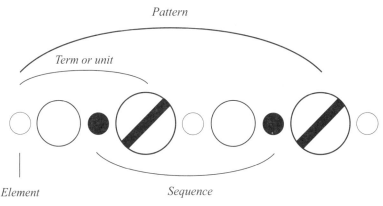

Figure 4

The recognition of a single entity remains the basis of all patterns, and their extension consists solely in the addition of a single unit, even if we redefine that unit as we do so.

However, for a moment we need to return to our original sequence. In a less graphical sense we would not be incorrect to discern a pattern here. We can easily recognize that all the elements are circles, enabling us to reinterpret them as units, and consequently to identify a five-term pattern, whereby simple repetition occurs four times, thus:

Figure 5 [2]

The circle is the unit; its differing graphical configuration in each term is simply an element of the content. This is fundamental to our perception of patterns in humour.

However, now consider the following pattern:

Figure 6

Initially we may assume this pattern exists solely in the simple reflection of a two-element term, but on closer inspection we can discern a more subtle method of repetition. Considering four terms instead of two, the same unit has been repeated but with one criterion of alteration between each term. The criterion in this case is rotation counter-clockwise by 90 degrees. In all other respects the units remain identical.

We will call this rotation the *criterion of repetition*. It is important to note at this point that not only has the unit been repeated with some level of translation, but the criterion of repetition has itself been repeated. Appearing first between units one and two, it is first repeated between units two and three, and then between three and four. Most individuals would have no problem if asked to predict the continuation of this pattern. A slightly less obvious example appears in Figure 7, where the angle of rotation is 30 degrees, preventing any single line of symmetry.

---

[2] Presenting the pattern in this abstract form is for illustrative purposes only. I am not implying that we reassemble it cognitively, nor that we require an abstract concept of the circle in order to recognize the similarity of terms beneath this pattern. Even if we could not define what constitutes a circle or had never encountered one before, the similarity of the characteristic *roundness* would be sufficient for us to see that it remains consistent throughout.

Figure 7

Whatever patterns we analyse, the situation remains the same, in that they consist of the repetition of a single unit with or without a level of translation referred to as the criterion. The criterion effects a level of alteration on the unit but enables it to remain within the pattern.

Certain criteria of repetition are familiar to us from other aspects of life: division is repetition in parts; multiplication is repetition of the whole; reflection, inversion, and reversal are all forms of repetition in opposite terms; translation is repetition in different media; minification and magnification are repetition on different scales.

Now consider the following two patterns:

Figure 8

Only the content of each pattern is different, and in all other respects they are in fact identical. The pattern is simple repetition, which might also be considered duplication in this case if we presume no continuation of the units will occur. The same criterion arises in each, and we could compound or complicate this criterion as many times as we liked. At no point, however, would the two patterns differ, regardless of the content we then projected onto them. The patterns in Figure 9 are identical.

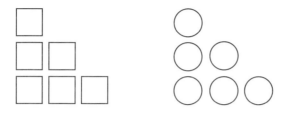

Figure 9

The addition of single units according to criteria of repetition can lead to complex patterns. Imagine for a moment wallpaper that has three different roses on it. If these apparently separate elements form a new unit, it will be altered uniformly by the criterion of the pattern. However, should the three roses each apply separate and differing criteria then we have, in fact, three different patterns occurring simultaneously. Instead, though, should the criteria applied by each differ by a set criterion itself, then we might produce something much more interesting. Either of these we might then refer to as a compound pattern. In certain situations it is possible to construct a compound pattern that in itself can be divided into a sequence of terms formed of a single unit, at which point it ceases to be a compound pattern once more.

To complicate things further, we could also decide to effect an alteration of the criterion of repetition in any single pattern by a set criterion in each stage, effectively producing a pattern of criteria. For example, to produce a rotation that increased by 30 degrees with each term, we could define the repetition as *criterion of term x = 30 degrees + criterion of term (x-1)*.

Throughout this book the individual unit is all important. From a simple singularity great complexity can be developed.

Sequences Of Triplicate Terms

Triplicate terms are very popular in humour for reasons that are founded in the basics of pattern recognition. We'll look at the practicality of this a little later.

Many patterns are the most simple possible, comprising only one element repeated with no criterion to effect its completion. Figure 10 is a pattern for our purposes but Figure 11 is not:

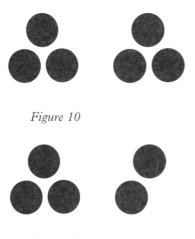

Figure 10

Figure 11

However, the sequence in Figure 11 has the potential for completion as a pattern by developing the criterion thus:

Figure 12

or even thus:

Figure 13

Yet in some common forms of repetition (reversal being the most obvious) the pattern exists as two single stages that do not involve repetition of the criterion, although they can of course be extended to involve this:

Figure 14

The first exhibits the same criterion as the second but in it neither the content nor the criterion is repeated without translation. We might say here that this is a simple recontextualized repetition.

However, some patterns require three stages in order to function as a pattern rather than a sequence. A temporal, unit-based revelation of the pattern in Figure 12 would initially present us with the three circles of the first stage, and then with Figure 11. At this point, although the criterion has been applied, we are uncertain what it is, since we might conclude with either Figure 12 or 13, or perhaps some other pattern as yet not considered for which the criterion is as yet unclear, rendering anticipation of the pattern open to interpretation. Just as importantly, though, it also masks the existence of a pattern, since this sequence has the potential to remain incomplete, either by continuing unpatterned, or perhaps by not continuing at all. Application of the third term closes this gap and confirms the identity of the operative criterion (or, as we shall later see, the criterion the individual presumes, or is intended to presume, to be operative), and confirms beyond doubt the existence of a pattern to be recognized. Interestingly, the use of triplicate terms pervades not just humour but rhetoric as well, being as it is the first multiplicity that allows the repetition of the criterion rather than the simple unit.

The Element Of Surprise

The occurrence of surprise is fundamental to the mechanism of humour, and is intricately entwined with the evolutionary benefits associated with its function. What does not surprise does not amuse, and the suddenness with which the individual recognizes a pattern heightens that surprise.

The degree to which we experience surprise is dependent upon innumerable cultural assumptions and personal idiosyncrasies. The individual's specific responses to countless variables, the vast majority of which will not be consciously recognizable at the time of the event, make it difficult to quantify or predict. Its role is to alert us to the appearance of new facts about the world around us, and to ensure that we are ready to deal with those facts as they appear. It is a corrective to invalid estimates of variables, or to defunct ideas and perceptions that have suddenly been rendered old-fashioned, highlighting that which must be absorbed into our worldview, into our new assessment of the environment. It can be produced by the appearance of something new or alternatively by the timing (subtle or otherwise) of an action or event, or by the disposition (momentary or otherwise) of the individual, even when the occurrence is quite quotidian. Although the process of humour operates at the level of the pattern, to this degree the delivery of that pattern will affect how we receive it, and consequently our tendency to be surprised by it. In all cases surprise arises because an occurrence or state is unexpected at that moment, but the content need be neither incongruous nor absurd.

This highlights its fundamental importance to humour.[3] Since surprise alerts us to unexpected alterations, laughter and the humorous response rewards us for recognition of patterns *despite those alterations*, thus rewarding us for cognitive perception in difficult circumstances, in unexpected places. We can therefore now say that *the humorous response is evoked by the surprise recognition of a pattern*.

Inevitably, then, exposure and experience become variables in the process of humour as experienced by an individual. Increased exposure to a stimulus (presuming habituation, or *long-term potentiation*, occurs) lessens our surprise at it, since we learn to include it in our assessment of what may, or is expected to, happen.

However, even if novelty is important for humour, the novelty of the stimulus need not be objectively true. Even the ablest of memories loses fidelity with time, despite the erroneous conviction that a perfect image

---

[3] It is no coincidence that clowns wear patterned clothes and produce sudden loud bangs, in what is essentially an externalized amalgam of the individual components of the mechanism of humour. The outward appearance of jesters and clowns is examined in greater detail in *Humour*.

of the stimulus has been maintained. On recognizing the pattern the second time around the individual may laugh once more, and is rewarded for rediscovering something that had been lost.

Assisted Recognition

The recognition of patterns is, in a great deal of comedy, assisted. Consistently mistaken for the source of humour itself, the *punch line* alerts us to the resolution of a pattern, or to the convergence of multiple patterns, and attempts to refine the moment of recognition to a sudden, surprising point. Although specific to linguistic humour, there are analogues in non-linguistic physical humour. Such analogues can not exist, however, in humour that is non-temporal, such as static photographs, although a single frame of a cartoon or other visual medium may attempt to draw the eye through a picture with the same intention. They are not, however, necessary, since pattern resolution may occur with or without them, and certain striking instances of modern comedy have removed them entirely. Laughter tracks and the drum flourishes of Vaudeville performances exist to heighten the moment of recognition further, as did the bells on the jester's bauble or *maharoof*.

Pattern recognition is also aided by the process of *anticipation and confirmation*. As described earlier, the use of triplicate terms is a common device in anticipation and confirmation since the individual expects the pattern to resolve but remains uncertain of the precise manner in which this will occur. The astute use of patterns that could potentially extend in two or more different ways lies at the centre of this technique.

For anticipation and confirmation to succeed, however, the individual must not be entirely convinced of their own predictions, otherwise surprise will not occur and the response will be muted. The nursery humour of *peek-a-boo* is the first example of such a device, and will be examined in more detail later.

Pattern Fidelity

After surprise, the individual's recognition of fidelity within the pattern will also affect the degree to which the stimulus is found amusing. Since humour lies in the recognition of patterns, the better the pattern as the individual sees it, the bigger the impact.

A common form of humour is the juxtaposition of two pictures, often photographs of people, that bear a surprising similarity to one another. The individual is struck by the ability to map the details of one onto the other (a simple pattern of repetition) when he or she would not have expected to be able to do so.[4] The greater the *pattern fidelity*, the funnier the individual will tend to find it. The more accurate the repetition, the more exact the pattern, and consequently the more surprising it becomes.

If the similarity between the two pictures lessens in some way, however, we will find this less amusing, all other factors of the stimulus and the individual remaining equal. Presume for the moment that the similarity hasn't lessened because of degradation to the photographs but because we have simply replaced one of them with a different picture. What we have degraded, of course, is the quality of the repetition, the fidelity of the pattern, that exists between their two terms. The human brain is capable of recognizing entities when substantially occluded to a remarkable degree not yet rivalled by anything that artificial intelligence has to offer, and although it will happily recognize a photograph that has been degraded, it has a thirst for fidelity of pattern, and is much less impressed by two vaguely similar photographs than by those that are nearly identical, even though it has the ability to *see what we mean* by the vague, degraded similarity.

However, if we return to our original two pictures but *mask* their similarity in some way, its recognition may be all the more surprising and the pattern fidelity would remain intact. It's important to remember that this masking, to render terms less recognizable, can not be achieved by lowering the quality of the pattern, since this does not have the same effect. If the similarity between the photos is not very great it will be harder to spot, but this doesn't make its recognition any funnier since the

---

[4] Mapping the faces of a father and his son might not be surprising if we have noticed or had reason to expect the similarity before, and, in the absence of ulterior pattern recognition, not therefore humorous.

fidelity of the pattern is diminished. The surprise, and how much we laugh, is therefore based upon how little we expect the pattern to apply (how little we expect the two photos to resemble each other) and the degree of fidelity identified within the pattern (how similar they actually are).

Consider again Figure 2, and our recognition of the pattern as one comprised of circles rather than of their graphical configurations, as per Figure 5. Changing the graphical content of each circle should not alter this recognition at all, and may well function as a mask to increase our surprise. However, we could degrade the fidelity of the same pattern by leaving a circle incomplete or squashing it into something much less precise. The pattern, that of circle repetition, would consequently have lost fidelity, although the individual may still be able to discern it, even though it would be considered less amusing, all other factors remaining equal.

Figure 15

Degrading it by replacing one of the circles with a triangle or a square, however, would leave the pattern very loose indeed, and quite possibly not discernible:

Figure 16

Pattern fidelity is a vital part of the process of humour, but it does not provide an objective measure of what is funny. Our ability to recognize fidelity (or *similarity*) varies, and our level of exposure to, and knowledge of, the content will affect our tendency to identify fidelity within a source (ut infra). I will most likely not find a caricature funny if I have never seen the person being lampooned, and if I have only seen them once or twice I may well still not be struck by the accuracy of the minification or magnification of their features. Conversely, I may know them very well indeed, and consider the artist's handiwork to be wildly inaccurate. Whether I am right or wrong, of course, despite being quite probably indeterminable in the majority of cases, is of no importance to the equation.

Complexity: Cross-media And Compound Patterns

The process of humour involves a huge number of variables, all dependent to some degree upon the individual receiving the stimulus. Its analysis is relatively straightforward at the level of stock formats but can quickly become complex when compounded and multiple patterns begin to dominate the material in question. The recognition of multiple patterns increases the humorous response, and complex combinations can lead to either obvious hilarity or *difficult*, subtle humour, depending on both the stimulus and the individual.

The majority of instances of humour employ more than one pattern. Regarding the juxtaposed pictures above, the individual's level of surprise will be heightened if their similarity is considered unexpected for some reason regarding their nature, or their occupation, or some other biographical detail. However, although this may imply the content is directly affecting the humour, we are in fact recognizing a second pattern underlying the juxtaposition. Incompatibility represents a simple case of opposition, which is recognized as reversal, or inversion, depending upon the detail, and similarity of some element, such as temperament, forms a further pattern of duplication. The individual must, of course, still be surprised by these ulterior structures or they will have no effect on the mechanism.

In the instances considered thus far, each pattern we have identified exists within a single medium. The photographs are static visuals, and any biographical detail is knowledge the individual possesses (although, as will be discussed later, this form of *translational mapping* is a little more complex than it first appears due the inclusion of the individual's memory as a term in the pattern). Humour, however, doesn't recognize these categories as boundaries to recognition, and regularly functions on a *cross-media* basis, building patterns from multiple sources. This is possible because the mechanism by which information is found amusing is identical in any format or medium. It is common for humorous sketches to feature single patterns composed of linguistic, physical, visual, and even auditory units in different orders. Humour recognizes patterns across any media, and once the pattern has been established it is possible for it to reverberate between them with less apparent repetition than in single-medium formats. Frequently, the use of such cross-media patterns also increases the surprise the individual experiences at their recognition.

The existence of multiple patterns, and the minutiae of delivery (such as intonation and timing) help to explain how an individual might find one production of a play much funnier than another, despite the dialogue remaining identical. The same patterns may continue to provide *potential sources of humour* in the text but the structures around them, and the addition of visual and physical patterns, can vary greatly, and delivery and presentation will alter both the individual's ability to recognize the patterns in the text and the degree of surprise they evoke. Again, the individual may think the same joke that was funny in the hands of one person falls flat when told by another. The minutiae of delivery, some of which affect the levels of surprise, some of which form their own patterns behind the words that are spoken, are fiddly, seemingly impenetrable elements in the analysis of humour. While I do not underestimate their contribution, they work on exactly the same basis as every other factor within the equation. Sometimes intonation and timing assist pattern recognition and heighten our surprise. Sometimes, used differently, they can degrade a pattern and detract from any surprise we might experience.

Recounting previously amusing situations is often affected in a similar way, leading to *you had to be there* syndrome, in which attempts to communicate the humour of a situation fail in their translation from several media (usually cross-media physical, visual and linguistic) to the single linguistic medium. Since the transmitter is incapable of acting out the entire scene, he or she supplies what is presumed to be the salient elements of the situation in linguistic form. The frequency of its failure is founded in the necessarily sequential and time-consuming nature of linguistic communication. Simultaneous occurrences can not be displayed, only explained, and the element of surprise is removed by both the slowness of speech and the narrative format of language. Further, the transmitter has no choice but to deselect a huge volume of information that would have been present at the time, choosing to communicate only those elements of the situation that caused their mirth. Without some knowledge of the workings of humour this is difficult to do, since the natural tendency is to relate the content, with little or no attention to the patterns underlying it.

Techniques Of Pattern Application And Combination

There are various forms in which patterns commonly interact that function well due to combinatory effects. Pattern persistence beyond information the individual expects to have dispelled it is formed by the cessation of the pattern being faked to some degree, and consequently its continuation is surprising. Similar is pattern resurgence, where, again, the individual presumes the pattern has concluded (whether the pattern in itself was surprising, and therefore humorous, or not) only to find it returns unexpectedly after a hiatus. The break revitalizes it, and its new context makes it all the more surprising. Reviving an earlier idea unexpectedly is a common form of wit, and appears frequently in improvised comedy.

Pattern interruption and usurpation involve the replacement of one pattern by another, and are frequently used to develop complex, compound patterns. In combination, the term that initiates the new pattern is often (but not necessarily) the concluding term of the previous one. A pattern in a repetitive stage may achieve cessation by the addition of a term that also resolves a previously unpatterned sequence, perhaps beginning a new stage of repetition of its own, which in itself could now form a *meta-pattern* with the earlier repetitive stage - a pattern of patterns, if you like.

Distraction by one supposedly dominant pattern can also make the revelation of another, previously unnoticed, more surprising and amusing. The surprise may be heightened by the individual's recognition of quite how active the pattern has been despite his or her failure to notice it while distracted. Unexpected pattern cessation, as we'll see later, is also a common form of humour. If the individual has grown accustomed to a pattern, whether it has produced humour or not at any point, the cessation of that pattern may generate surprise by its sudden closure. Combining these two processes produces dual recognition of current cessation and retrospective activity and could, of course, be further compounded by a new pattern, immediately recognizable, supplanting the old as per usurpation.

In some instances of humour the individual is supplied with an event that has some of the information missing. *Noises off* or actions in darkness are common formats, where the partial picture presented is translated from the medium of the humour and repeated in the mind of the individual, where it is reassembled as a whole unit, a complete entity. Depending upon what is envisaged, and how quickly it is envisaged, the individual may be surprised, and find the completion amusing. This technique is commonly combined with others, especially multiple-stage simple repetition regarding the incomplete information with which we are provided. We will refer to this as *provoked completion*. It is similar to the humorously-neutral *entity completion* discussed later, except that in *provoked completion* the process of completion is not performed for us, and our completion of the unit forms an active term within a pattern. Since a unit can be added to a sequence in any circumstances and, perhaps, by doing so, produce a pattern to be recognized, completion occurs frequently in the mind of the individual when not overtly employed as a device by the originator, and accounts for a great deal of what is unique about a person's sense of humour. This second type we will refer to as *unprovoked completion*.

The Individual: Interpretative Scope And The Connotative Expanse

The individual is absolutely central to the process of humour. Comedians may attempt to produce ready-made packages that include all the elements of humour, but they can not, in fact, do so. The role of error, of experience, of meta-meaning, perception, location and interpretation in the observer render comedians little more than *transmitters* of patterns they have recognized, and the individual may or may not find humour within them.

Different levels of surprise exist according to exposure and retention, and different experiences mean patterns may be recognized with a different level of fidelity (if at all) and perhaps a different interpretation. The recognition of different patterns where multiple potentials exist (which may be everywhere depending upon terms of knowledge) mean we can all find ourselves laughing at different things at the same time; indeed, it is possible to recognize patterns anywhere, or to construct them ourselves from the scraps we find in the outside world in *unprovoked completion*. It is quite possible for people of varying degrees of age and ability to find exactly the same material funny for different reasons, being surprised by different patterns depending upon their knowledge and levels of observation.

Since much of the mechanism of humour relies upon the individual's comprehension of similarity, responses will depend upon the degree to which two terms are estimated to be similar, and this depends heavily on knowledge and understanding of the subject matter. On closer examination, two supposedly identical items will inevitably be found to differ more than originally perceived. One of the basic processes of intellect, underpinning all cognition and information processing, is differentiation. To an outsider with no interest in a recording artist two different songs may sound identical, but to a fan they might appear wildly different since every nuance has been observed, registered and cherished.

Methods of personal hierarchization are necessarily individual because of tastes, priorities and knowledge. Even simple categories of similar terms are difficult to homogenize. The simple repetition of *Dog ~ Dog ~ Dog* may be developed into *Poodle ~ Labrador ~ Bulldog*, and most people would agree that both include three sets of similar terms, both of which exhibit precise fidelity if all we require is reference to any dog, but of which only one, the former, displays precision if we require reference to a specific breed. However, *Dog ~ Cat ~ Budgerigar*, although at first imprecise, is simply a repetition of similar terms within a pattern of domestic pets, and *Dog ~ Cat ~ Monkey* features exactly the same pattern, repeating similar terms within a pattern of mammals. It is the individual, though, not the zoological taxonomic, the Dewey Decimal, the analytico-synthetic or any other variety of formal classification that determines what is considered to be similar, and this regularly obscures the identity of the patterns at which another person is laughing. In order to be able to recognize a pattern the individual must first be able to comprehend what constitutes an entity within it.

Traditionally, stand-up comedy features *translational mapping* in the form of *it's so true* humour. For sound theoretical reasons individuals tend to laugh more when the subject matter relates to them or their situation, their companions or their interpretation of the world. The operative pattern is not dissimilar to our two juxtaposed photographs that appear so amusingly alike, since we note the surprising similarity between life and its representation, between the stimulus and the mental image we maintain of it. For any instance, a simple mapping of the individual's life experience on top of other patterns will increase their appreciation of the stimulus beyond that of someone who fails to identify these similarities, all other factors being equal. Hence the closer to the individual's life the stimulus appears to be, the more amusing it will be found, in addition to any other patterns which may or may not in themselves stimulate a response. The surprising element of this pattern, of course, lies in both the novel manner in which the comedian communicates the information and the fact that the information, usually unarticulated, is being communicated at all. The detail of the individual's memory is consequently itself a term within the pattern, a *re-cognition* of the entity translated by the stimulus.

The suspension of the triplicate term referred to in pattern interruption and analysis, and the potential for pattern completion of any material, accounts partly for the manner in which multiple individuals may respond to the same stimulus for quite different reasons, with confusion sometimes arising when the differing interpretations are compared. They have, in fact, identified different *sources* of humour within the same *stimulus*, the interpretation of which will be further individualized by the particular associations retained mentally by each regarding the material. Although the objective stimulus remains the same, the individual's perception of the stimulus is unique.

Just as individuals possess specific terms of reference, associations and connotations (a single word can evoke memories or ideas for an individual not shared by any other person), so too, in a broader sense, do cultures and societies, and those associations change with time as the culture develops and alters its priorities. Because of this, popular comedy can be produced that appeals to millions but, equivalently, humour from a different age can appear decidedly unamusing. In order to be able to perceive patterns we require some level of familiarity with the subject matter. In the alien world of the past, even if we appear to understand the content, the deterioration of pattern fidelity due to shifts in meaning linguistically or socially, the absence of cultural references and associations to reinforce expectations and to provide ulterior patterns, and the inevitable alterations in levels of surprise and shock at certain subject matters, can all combine to render the comedy *outdated*. The most persistent comedy is that which has exposed its patterns in a manner which is still discernible in a different age, whether by commonality of subject matter, transparency of formation or coincidence of circumstance.

However, regardless of our interpretative tendency, behind the content the mechanism of humour remains identical throughout both the ages and the continents, as do the patterns underlying it, and is the same for every individual.

The Question Of Illustration

The full-length book provides extensive illustration and analysis not possible here, documenting the association of pattern type with format of humour in multiple media. Certain stock formats utilize standard pattern types and combinations on a frequent basis, and a few rely exclusively on one or two. Certain forms of humour have been produced to expose the patterns intended by their originators more readily than others, various examples of which play a formative role in childhood cognitive development.

However, only stock formats of humour can be neatly matched to predetermined pattern formations in this manner, and in other instances we have to analyse the individual elements of each stimulus in isolation, extrapolating the terms involved with care, since complex, compounded patterns can be readily developed from the basic repertoire.

There is, of course, a difficulty involved in communicating the mechanism of an instance of humour via this clinical form of illustration if humour is, as it must be, an individual, subjective reaction and consequently not definable in terms of inherent properties. In order to compensate for this, and to avoid falling into the pitfalls and implications of psychometric *comprehension*, we will discern the most obvious patterns behind the illustrations only, without any presumption that the remaining mechanism will necessarily produce humour. Many further patterns could be identified by the individual, but we will restrict ourselves in these examples to an attempted identification of those the originator of the stimulus appears to have *intended* us to recognize. While anything is potentially amusing, it is the ability to discern patterns as others might see them that will determine the accurate application of this theory, not the ability to be amused by the stimulus under examination or to produce an exhaustive catalogue of the patterns appearing in any stimulus. Since no such catalogue can exist, and since none of those we identify may apply to any individual, we will refer to these patterns, as we identify them, as *potential sources of humour*.

We will continue here with two succinct examples of stock linguistic formats.

Illustration: Punning

Before we establish our model we must briefly examine the role of *entity completion*, in which an element is completed by another, forming a whole unit, a single entity. Although it is not strictly a pattern, a completed unit must necessarily include again all those elements present during its incomplete stage, so it is possible to see this, too, as a form of repetition.

Unlike *provoked* and *unprovoked completion*, however, completion of an entity is neutral in humour, and only functions in combination with other pattern types. It is a foil for patterns, an entity we apprehend in a surprising manner while dominant patterns function in and around it. Although it may indeed appear that isolated entity completion is occasionally the source of humour, closer inspection will reveal the existence of an ulterior, unnoticed pattern functioning in tandem alongside it, such as simple reversal or, just as frequently, minification or magnification. Hence a surprising answer to a question is only a potential source of humour if it attaches itself to an active pattern in combination.

Our stock format here is punning, so I have chosen a common pun in joke form as my illustration:

What do ghouls eat? Poached eggs on ghost!

This presents us with two simultaneous patterns that may form a potential source of humour:

What do ghouls eat? Poached eggs on toast.
(Subservient pattern, or *entity completion*, consisting of a question that is completed in an expected or unsurprising manner.)

ghouls   *ghost*

(Dominant pattern of repetition in similar terms.)

We are asked to complete the hidden (subservient) pattern as our brains would expect to understand it (the food you might eat is *poached eggs on toast*, not *ghost*), but simultaneously to recognize the repetition of similar terms between ghouls and ghosts. The second, dominant pattern completes the entity of the first with an element of alteration that is intended to surprise us, and in the single word *ghost*, both patterns are resolved.

It is essential to this stock format that the dominant pattern is more important than the subservient one. Ghouls can *eat* anything they like, as long as we recognize it as *food* (and consequently as a reasonable completion of the question and answer entity), but the element of repetition in the dominant pattern must repeat the similar terms of the subject. *Ghouls* could eat *ghosted sandwiches*, for example, but not *poached eggs on coast*, despite the transparency of the completed entity to which we are referring. The reason for this, as mentioned above, is that the process of *entity completion* remains neutral.

However, despite its neutrality and subservience, the entity we are asked to complete, hidden behind the dominant pattern, must remain recognizable when affected by the resolution. The phonological similarity of *toast* and *ghost* enables us to identify the entity in its unsurprising form and consequently to recognize its unexpected alteration by the dominant pattern. For example, the structure of the pun would be affected if we concluded it with *poached eggs on spooks*, despite the dominant pattern remaining intact, since without a level of transparency we will not readily recognize the subservient pattern. Again, *ghosts* can't *eat coddled ghost* or *eat duck a la ghost* since, although surprising, this does not maintain the fidelity of the entity, despite the fidelity of the dominant pattern exhibiting perfection.

This leads us onto the subject of duality of meaning in linguistic jokes where the repetition is non-destructive. In the sort of punning illustrated here, the existence of the two patterns is necessarily destructive since their resolution is dependent upon similar, but essentially different, terms. In *Humour* we will examine the patterns involved in simple, but surprising, non-destructive recontextualization, and illustrate how they relate to many other types of non-linguistic and non-verbal humour.

Illustration: Sarcasm

For our second model I have chosen sarcasm. Presume for one moment that I am being sarcastic when I write:

I really like your tie.

Here, if we recognize this as sarcasm, we recognize *what is not* as a potential source of humour. It is a basic pattern of reversal, a translational repetition in opposites, whether we term it reversal or inversion. The recognition of an opposition requires the recognition of both competing terms, regardless of the fact that they exist in different media: the first in the words I have spoken, the second in your mind. On comparison the recognition that they are the reversal of each other produces the potential for humour.

This sort of sarcasm could be referred to as *simple sarcasm*, since it consists of only one pattern. However, now consider the following statement:

I like your tie so much I'm going to buy a thousand so I never run out.

Now we have a form of *compound* sarcasm, where the basic reversal is supported by the pattern of magnification, where the comparison of scale between two or more terms provides the potential for humour: in this case the term in your mind estimating the number of ties a person might reasonably purchase of the same pattern, and the term consisting of my exaggerated equivalent. Magnification and minification are strong, easily recognized patterns, providing readily assimilated comparisons, and their use in compound sarcasm makes our recognition that the person is in fact being sarcastic a little easier.

This all leads us to the potential pitfalls inherent in the deployment of sarcasm. Since sarcasm is fundamentally lying, its use of everyday structures means that it has the potential to be mistaken as a truthful statement, failing to register with the recipient. Returning to our illustration of simple sarcasm above, unless you have a reason to recognize the reversal of the truth you will also fail to recognize my sarcasm. Your reasons for suspecting the reversal may consist of your knowledge of my tastes, your recognition of how ugly your tie really is, or simply the intonation I employ, the inappropriate nature of which might alert you to an excess, or complete lack, of enthusiasm in my statement. The use of the latter could potentially form a further pattern, this time of opposite terms: the enthusiasm of my tone and the enthusiasm of my statement.

Since simple sarcasm is the least readily identifiable form, it is possible to flatter a person sarcastically without their ever becoming cognisant of your views. Indeed, it is often only when they are alerted to an ulterior pattern, of magnification perhaps, or simple repetition, that the existence of the first becomes apparent. Indeed, for this reason sarcasm often escalates throughout a conversation while the sarcastic transmitter attempts to add more terms to the meta-pattern of increasingly extreme repetitions of scale and reversal to bring it to a resolution in the form of the subject's recognition of its nature.

Further, since sarcasm functions in the same way as any other instance of humour, it may not be found amusing if it simply isn't surprising. If you know all too well what I think about your tie the pattern of reversal will not surprise you, unless I construct it elaborately and unpredictably and catch you unawares. Since the individual may either fail to identify the pattern intended or not be surprised by its recognition, sarcasm is frequently enjoyed more by associates of the transmitter (who are aware of the views of the transmitter and have evidence of their reversal in the subject but are surprised, nonetheless, to hear the sarcastic person lying in such a confrontational manner) than its intended recipient.

The normal recognition of a lie elsewhere in life, however, is not generally viewed as a source of humour. Beyond the inappropriate nature of the psychological state discussed later (see *Suppression And Denial*), there are further reasons for this. There is usually uncertainty surrounding the nature of a lie, and our recognition of its falsehood is often gradual and piecemeal, removing any of the surprise associated with humour. However, we should presume from our model that certain lies are capable of evoking laughter when they are suddenly apprehensible and not mood-forming, and this is the case, as is often evidenced when small children tell patent lies without any humorous intention on their part. The more obvious the lie the greater the potential it has as a source of humour, since the patency of its nature makes our recognition of it faster, and suddenness of recognition, as already discussed, heightens the surprise the individual will experience.

Although some of the patterns examined in these two short illustrations have been compounded, each one individually has consisted of no more than two terms (excepting our touching briefly on meta-patterns). In *Humour* we will progress from similar two-term types in other linguistic formats to multi-term, compounded cross-media patterns from many other media.

The Ontogenic Mechanism And The Function Of The Joke

As adults we are keen to pass on our enjoyment of humour to infants. The impulse to do so, to attempt to make them laugh, is strong from an early age, and the infant generally obliges us somewhere between the ages of three and four months. Assertions that this laughter is unconnected to humour are the product of misconceptions regarding its mechanism (such as McGhee, 2002; Provine, 1992; Kris, 1939).

The most common process by which the adult first encourages a humorous response is that of visual pattern display.[5] In the infantile *peek-a-boo* (one of various equivalents all producing the same effect) it is the sudden appearance of another term in the pattern of simple visual repetition that provides the potential source of humour. A certain level of anticipation and confirmation exists within the game, but, as in adults

[5] It is possible that there are precursors to these physical games involving the rhythmic intonation of *baby talk*, although it becomes difficult at these earlier stages to distinguish the cooing of appreciation and smiling exhibited by babies in normal contented appreciation from a humorous response, which may for many reasons not yet be fully developed.

also, if the extension of the pattern does not surprise with each term, depending on the precise mechanics of the reappearance, the child does not laugh. The child remains not *entirely* certain that the next term will occur, and the ability to deny its expectations heightens the effect of the humour. Early instances of play, when the child is first exposed to the structure of the game, are gentle and unsurprising in order not to startle the child, and the first laugh of each new game is almost always weaker than those to follow, since the basic pattern of repetition has not yet been established. Older infants who are well versed in the game may well even laugh in expectation of the next term of the pattern before it has appeared, previewing the event in their imaginations in *unprovoked completion*.

One of the major differences between infantile and adult humour is the seeming indefatigability of interest the child exhibits in the repetition of identical stimuli or patterns. The *do it again* element of childish humour is known to all who have cared for them, since the nascent memory renders such repetitious play more attractive, the activity of which may potentially contribute to the development of the memory itself. With lower levels of habituation, the patterns involved remain attractive much longer than they do for an adult, who will almost always tire of such play before the infant. Improvements in memory throughout childhood have uncertain, and most probably numerous, causes but it is almost unarguable that increases in the capacity of working memory are an important part of cognitive development. Eventually, however, if the adult can persist for long enough, even the child tires of the stimulus and a new distraction is sought.

It is no coincidence that the earliest incidences of laughter elicited by *peek-a-boo* (whether they involve the use of an inanimate object or simple *presence and absence* or *looming* of the adult) arise at about four months (Montague & Walker-Adams, 2001), at which point the memory is developing sufficiently for infants to be able to represent objects in their visual short-term memory, but only one at a time. Further, between three and five months they develop the ability "to encode and remember location" such as the "location of an object when it was hidden and then revealed" (Oakes & Bauer, 2007). Patterns exist because of repetition, and without short term memory there can be no recognition of connected terms that are presented in a temporal manner. As the child matures, the intervals between the terms of the pattern may be lengthened with no loss of humour, reflecting the advance in their short-term memories, and the game becomes especially enjoyable for the infant between the ages of about seven and nine months, when inanimate toys are usually employed to embellish the fleeting process.

At the age of about six months a new game arises which evokes laughter for a certain period in most infants, commonly known as *clap hands*. This is composed of a compound pattern, the first of the temporal repetition between each individual clap, and the second of the spatial *reflection* between the infant and its companion. It constitutes one of the first games of true mutuality, in which the infant usually progresses to initiate future play. If two adult individuals clap hands it may not be surprising, but to an infant it is the first sight of mutual pattern formation, of interaction in the production of a game, and the reflective format provides the first exposure to patterns that are surprising yet not solely temporal. However, the predictable nature of the process and its often rhythmic regularity mean that the overt humorous response is sometimes lost from this game relatively quickly, and it becomes instead a form of reassurance, a confirmatory link between the infant and the outside world, as, indeed, it continues to be throughout adult life.

Towards the end of the first year the infant moves onto the next fundamental step in humorous development. Until this point the child's interaction with the world has largely consisted of observation and familiarization, handling and mouthing objects and becoming acquainted with the environment around them through its different sensory mechanisms. As a consequence, with the exception of mutual play such as *clap hands*, sources of humour have generally been provided for it by external stimuli. However, at some point between nine months and a year the child begins to create its own humorous amusement in the generic form of *building block demolition*, which is initially either taught to the child or undertaken of its own accord. Sometimes consisting of different, analogous content, this version is widespread and ideally illustrates the fundamentals of the genre. The anticipation and confirmation involved in the gradual development of the construction function as they do elsewhere in humour, the sudden resolution when the tower is finally destroyed, and the unpredictable elements of how and where the blocks fall, regardless of whether it is the child or an adult who has knocked over the construction, contribute greatly to the infant's surprise and enjoyment. Finally, the importance of repeating the demolition must not be overlooked. First exposure to the game, again, may startle the infant, but once a pattern has been established the game evokes a humorous response for as long as the child remains surprised by the moment of demolition and its consequences. When undertaken entirely by the infant, this stage represents the first example of the child in isolation manipulating the physical world for humorous rewards.

It is worth considering that the first three major steps of humour in infancy, *peek-a-boo*, *clap hands* and *building block demolition*, are not only important as we can see in relation to humour, but are also reflective of, and simultaneous with, major steps in the infant's cognitive development. This is, of course, no coincidence.

A fourth source of humour in toddlers is the moment at which a person with whom they are familiar pulls a face. The first three instances set up, in predictable order, the surprise apprehension of an entity in repetition, then its extension into mutuality and spatial reflection, and then a more complex, multi-stage game in which the toddler contributes a part (or sometimes all) of the process, yet this fourth is the first example of the infant patently recognizing recontextualization. The pattern we are identifying here is not the visual pattern adumbrated by the distorted facial features, but the pattern of repetition produced by the similar identity of the face-puller in different contexts. Despite the alteration in the physical appearance, the pattern is recognized in this surprising situation. Consequently this form of humour is only usually acceptable to infants when it is presented by someone with whom they are familiar. Unfamiliar faces present no pattern of repetition to young infants if the recognition of similar identity does not occur, leading frequently to disorientation and potential upset. Evidence suggests that infants six months and younger would be unable to appreciate such humour from an unfamiliar person because until this age they are unable to store the visual appearance of more than one object in short term memory (Ross-Sheehy, Oakes & Luck, 2003), although infants younger than this may prove capable of appreciating it from an adult they know well. However, it is also likely that, during later development, pattern recognition also occurs between the face and other objects it is seen to resemble, producing a compound pattern of dual repetition, the first of identity translated temporally from the normal face as witnessed to the mental image of that same face once it has changed, the second of coincident similarity between the adumbration of the face and another entity retained mentally by the individual.

As the child matures, however, they tend to grow out of such games since the development of the scaffold and physiology of memory renders them, for the most part, predictable and unhumorous. The ability to speak fluently, to categorize the external world with some degree of accuracy leads to the next stage of ontogenic humour.

Children tend to begin to grapple with linguistic humour (as opposed to humour transmitted in the verbal medium) at around the age of four or five years, yet there is normally little initial success, and many children will fail to become proficient until the ages of seven or eight (Kolb, 1990). Despite the brain's ability to produce a humorous response to stimuli of surprising patterns in the external world, the development of its linguistic form entails essentially a relearning, in a different form of representation, of the same basic principles. Despite exhibiting apparently normal, if undeveloped, cognitive ability elsewhere, the strictures of linguistic humour evade young children. Fortunately, help is at hand. The joke is the staple social format of humour since it adheres to basic patterns and structures, and is consequently readily accessible, with the ultimate system of assisted recognition, the *punch line*, neatly integrated to emphasize the intentions of the originator. As such it represents the perfect vehicle via which to communicate the artistry of linguistic humour in predictable and unchanging formats.

This leads, inevitably, to a question of the origin of humour in infants. Since I am convinced that the acquisition of linguistic humour is the result of social education, we are faced with the question of whether the earlier, non-linguistic development is also the result of interaction, or whether these cognitive processes are ultimately innate, and only their translation into the representative medium requires external input. We will examine this further in *The Recapitulative Question*.

Interestingly, the early developmental stages of linguistic humour reflect the assembly of the humorous mechanism in an exposed manner that would be difficult to analyse to the same extent in its non-linguistic neonatal counterpart. In our first illustration above we saw how *surprise entity completion* is necessary for some forms of linguistic wit but neutral in its effects: it is a sort of foil, a background on which to drape patterns. Interestingly, it arises in childhood, where it does indeed appear to evoke a humorous response. It occurs while the child is first learning the process by which linguistic humour is formed, before the combination of patterns required for, say, punning, is fully grasped. Taking a joke to which it has been exposed, the child attempts to manufacture its own resolution while retaining the same stem structure. Instead of achieving resolution, however, the child simply appends any word considered surprising, despite its irrelevance to the dominant pattern, thus:

What do ghouls like to eat? Poached eggs on chairs!

The entity has simply been completed in a surprising manner, and to most adults there would be little humour here since the dominant pattern has been omitted. The child searches for increasingly surprising alternatives and can do so, seemingly amused, for hours:

Or houses! Or dogs! Or bus stops!

A later stage in punning, but which often precedes this stage in other forms of joke, features mimicry of the resolution's phonological similarity to the dominant pattern, since it is presumed that the secret of the humour lies in the sound, rather than the meaning, of the word:

What do ghouls like to eat? Poached eggs on host! Or boast! Or boats! Or goats!

It is not, surprising, however, that the child fails to find an alternative resolution we consider acceptable, since the stem has usually been retained in its entirety, with perhaps only one or two words of alteration at its conclusion. However, since laughter is usually evoked by the resolution of a joke, the child searches for the method by which it functions at that point exclusively, presuming the stem to be of little or no importance.

Those who have witnessed children during this process will perhaps have noted them pausing and laughing, sometimes explosively, as they identify a reason to justify their choice of resolution, recognizing, apparently, patterns of their own imagination during *unprovoked completion*.

It is difficult to tell, however, whether the child is genuinely amused during this process or whether their laughter is mimetic, reproducing the pleasure they have witnessed adults and older siblings deriving from jokes. I suspect in most cases there is humour occurring here, although whether it is based on the process of simple entity completion so clearly neutral by adulthood, or the recognition of other completed patterns in their imaginations, I am uncertain. Although it would remain consistent with this theory for simple entity completion to produce humour at developmental stages, I am unconvinced that it would be necessary as a reward to encourage further application. The child has already experienced what it is to laugh and what it is to find things funny, and would surely be keen to utilize an entirely new source of humour he or she has witnessed others appreciating around them regardless of a neurological incentive along the way. Besides, as discussed in *Revising Assumptions About Humour's Social And Communicative Roles*, there may be other rewards the child is now seeking from proficiency with linguistic humour not provided by the humorous response itself.

The existence of this stage in development was predicted from the basic tenets of this theory, since we can only comprehend a pattern if we can first apprehend the entities of which it is composed, and was later confirmed by observation. Whether it has a neonatal, non-linguistic counterpart, however, is as yet unclear.

Eventually, with some level of correction by associated adults, the child learns the basic formats associated with linguistic humour, and is able to comprehend their content to the satisfaction of the originators. In this manner a joke becomes a simple paradigm for infantile development, bridging the gap between the very simplest graphical recognition of early infancy and the complex, cross-media pattern recognition of adulthood, assimilating the newly acquired linguistic skills into the humorous repertoire.

Conscious Analogues To Humour

Humour is an unconscious system, which has remained one of the major bars to our comprehension of its mechanism. We may be able to identify the stimulus of the humour that has amused us, but the hidden nature of the patterns means that in most cases we have been unable to identify the source.

Without the burden of attention many more calculations can be performed in unconscious cognition than in its conscious counterpart. Some forms of optical illusion, however, are a form of conscious analogue to humour displaying many of the traits of its mechanism at a much slower pace, and in a much more obvious fashion. For centuries humankind has amused itself with illusions, and some of the most diverting, and the most appropriate here, are those that feature *ambiguous depictions*, the most common examples being a drawing that viewed in one way appears to be a duck but in another appears to be a rabbit, and a vase that when examined differently depicts two opposing faces. Also much celebrated is the Necker cube, displaying the same kind of reversal in depth. When the individual first encounters these illusions he or she will generally only perceive one or other of the possibilities, since the brain settles on one of the rival interpretations of sensory data. When told there is an alternative manner in which to process the information, however, the individual searches for it consciously, attempting to reapply precisely the same visual configuration to a different interpretation. When this is achieved, the picture appears to mutate, and the individual sees it in its alternative form.

While I accept that ambiguous optical illusions are entertaining (otherwise they would not exist outside psychology departments), I am not claiming that they constitute humour as we know it elsewhere, for which there are very good reasons (although they have been known to produce a mild chuckle on first exposure). The process of repeating exactly the same information (the lines on the page) establishes a pattern of perfect fidelity (precise repetition) which surprises the individual because the impact of the visual changes. This entire process mimics the basic mechanism by which humour functions, but at a much slower rate than is generally exhibited when the individual finds things humorous. Again, although the new context of the same information surprises us, we have consciously sought it out having been alerted to its existence, inevitably reducing the surprise we experience at its recognition. Ambiguities of this kind, as diverting as they may be, rely on one central pattern, but it should not be overlooked that the individual will also be more or less impressed by the illusion depending upon the basic fidelity of each interpretation of the sensory data to objects retained mentally. If the individual first notices the duck and, after some effort, recognizes its alternative state as a rabbit but considers this second rendering unconvincing, he or she will be less amused by the whole endeavour.

Over the years, criticisms have been levelled at incongruity theories on the basis that they fail to explain the difference between solving a problem and finding something amusing. Although they are largely incorrect, this particular criticism evaporates if one emphasizes the distinction between conscious and unconscious processes. Problem solving is inherently conscious and laboured, and humour is unconscious, sudden and surprising. Further, without wishing to blur the boundaries here, some problem solving does indeed appear to evoke a mild humorous response, and we should now be able to identify the reasons those relevant instances do so.

Surprise *double meaning* could be seen as a precise humorous analogue to such ambiguous optical illusions but there is also a similar, non-linguistic form. In optical illusions, the configuration remains the same but our perception changes, whereas, in its humorous analogue, *pulling face*s, the configuration changes but our perception remains the same.

Function

The Evolutionary Benefits And Functions of Humour

We will need to return to the basic stipulations of the mechanism here, which are:

The apprehension of entities and their surprising recognition in pattern form: the mechanism of pattern recognition is the process by which entities are first apprehended and then reassessed in adapted circumstances. The identity of a unit is first perceived, followed by comprehension of that unit in an adapted state. By this process of recognition we learn to apply similar patterns to different terms, and to identify similar terms in different patterns.

Consider for a moment a brief narrative scenario revolving around a hominoid ancestor of modern humans. We will presume (however erroneously) that the hominoid species were hunter-gatherers, or that, at the very least, they were omnivorous opportunists. Entering a clearing a lone male proceeds to a small stretch of water he recognizes from previous visits several months beforehand. On bending to drink he

51

notices his reflection and uses it to tend to a wound he has received on his cheek, simultaneously recognizing the image as a *representation* of an animate being of his own species and as himself in spatial reflection. This may be nothing so remarkable, and almost certainly nothing for us to laugh at. Chimpanzees are able to use mirrors to groom themselves (Gallup, 1982; Essock-Vitale & Seyfarth, 1986), and orang-utans can recognize themselves in reflections also (interestingly, though, gorillas are unable to discriminate between a representation and the physical world, and consequently presume their reflection to be another gorilla with whom to interact). Recent research has also suggested that elephants are capable of achieving the same cognitive feat (Plotnik, de Waal & Reiss, 2006), yet it is worth noting that human infants appear unable to recognize themselves in a mirror until the age of about eighteen months. In fact, this simple case of reflection is more complex than it might at first appear, since it is cross-media, requiring our translation of the pattern from three dimensions to a two-dimensional representation.

Our male hominoid does not laugh, and neither would we, since we would be unsurprised by this simple pattern of reflection, and have been accustomed to this form of representation since infancy. However, it is only a small step from this perception to an entertainment that has been amusing individuals for centuries at funfairs, functioning on exactly the same principle but compounding it with two further elements. I am referring, of course, to the *hall of mirrors*. The distortion of certain areas of the reflection adds at least one further pattern to the reflective stimulus – that of magnification or minification, and provides the possibility for repetitive patterns of translational similarity between the image as viewed and other entities retained by the individual's mind. The unfamiliarity of the reflections, and the order in which they appear, provides the element of surprise usually missing in the process of observing one's reflection at home.

Patterns are not, of course, an artificial, modern construct, and neither are their distortion. Wherever any repetition exists, whether of an action or an element, patterns do too. The benefit of an ability to recognize patterns in unexpected or alien places, or in surprising events or objects, is an invaluable cognitive tool. Furthermore, patterns are not simply created by the alignment of terms in the physical world; they are created by our own actions too, whether temporally or spatially or both, and our circumstances and orientation create patterns of interaction with the world around us that, if recognized, could be of benefit to us in our processes of manipulation.

Looking back to Figure 6, the example of 90 degrees counter-clockwise rotation is swiftly assimilated from our static viewpoint. However, humans are locomotive species, and our ability to assimilate and process information from the world around us is continually challenged not only by alterations in environment but also by alterations in our own location and orientation. The pattern in Figure 6 could just as easily occur because of *our* alteration of circumstances, where the term of the pattern is in fact remaining static, and we are rotating 90 degrees *clockwise* at certain intervals. We would still recognize the same entity, though, effectively compensating for our own subjectivity as pattern recognition does.

Returning to our hunter-gatherer, we find something has caught his attention. While nursing his wound in the water, he has noticed a duck (or a similarly edible bird) sleeping at some distance on the opposite bank. He had previously been unaware of its existence because it was, and still is, hidden beneath leafy foliage, and considers itself safe from predators. But humans are clever animals, and despite the fact that the bird is well hidden and at a distance, our hunter-gatherer recognizes its minified, reflected (and therefore reversed) representation while holding his head at 90 degrees from the perpendicular. The sudden revelation of the same object in a different form (from the basics of face-pulling to characters who break free from their concealment against a supposedly inanimate backdrop) is a frequent technique in visual humour, as we would predict, closely replicating as it does the early evolutionary function of humour.

There are few (if any) other animals who could have made such a translation of the stimulus into this extrapolated interpretation. Pattern recognition's *contentless* operation means that it is endlessly adaptable, and new information, any new information, may be assessed by it in a fraction of a second.

So what of humour? This swift, unconscious execution of pattern recognition in the environment is identical in mechanism to the process by which humour is absorbed. The humorous response occurs in a split second, and if conscious interpretation of the stimulus occurs it does so subsequently and generally without attention to the underlying patterns. The workings are transferred to the unconscious to save time, only erupting to alert the individual to the moment of recognition and to encourage the pursuit of similar rewards.

It must not be forgotten that it is not the content that evokes the humorous response but the patterns underlying it. Even in a previously unfamiliar environment or an alien object, pattern recognition enables us to apprehend elements and structures beneath the unidentifiable entity. Our recognition of patterns exists to make sense of a world in which everything is ultimately bewilderingly unique. To this degree, humour is an analytical tool, the ability to apprehend entities and to recognize them when recontextualized. As a locomotive, conscious explorer this has obvious benefits, but on a wider scale it affords a problem-solving capacity with a level of flexibility not present in other animals. Once we are used to seeing our duck in a different context, it is only a sideways step to seeing a new, previously unknown object in the duck's place once it has been hunted to extinction.

Despite having been wrong-footed by the alteration of the stimulus (whether environmental habitat or linguistic construct), the individual is rewarded for nonetheless managing to discern patterns (to interpret familiar aspects) behind the alien material (the unfamiliar territory). Life is shifting and uncertain, yet adaptability is encouraged from the most basic of cognitive operations, providing the individual with a seemingly effortless, continual method of reassessment by which to adapt to changing environments, to previously unknown content and ideas, entities or states. *Hence humour rewards us for cognitive perception in difficult circumstances.*

Also, just as a faculty to encourage the recognition of patterns in our hominoid's environment would doubtlessly assist his chances of survival, so would the application of that same faculty to their cessation. Just as we should recognize patterns, we should recognize their absence if this is surprising to us too, and we find this to be borne out by instances of humour, frequently in pattern *cessation* and *usurpation*, but also in the pattern *frustration* associated with absurdist humour. Our recognition of changes in environment are important, especially if we have grown so accustomed to everyday patterns that we no longer recognize them, and the cessation of one positive pattern need not necessarily be associated with the incursion of an ulterior, more deleterious counterpart. Being able to overlook the continuation of a harmless, mundane pattern until its alteration alerts us to its existence is a highly economical cognitive tool. Yet, of course, the end of that pattern must surprise us if we are to notice its cessation. What does not surprise us we expect to be the norm, of which we already have an understanding.

The recognition of a pattern is of fundamental importance to our survival, for everything from locating and securing food to social interaction. Yet were we to be rewarded just the same for the recognition of an old pattern as we were for the recognition of a new one, there would be no reason to develop, for staring at the same two trees from infancy onwards would invoke the same neurophysiologically rewarding high for as long as we were lucky to survive. This is not how humour functions, though, and the role of surprise in pattern recognition ensures we are only rewarded for that which is fundamentally revelatory. The apprehension of the unexpected is intricately entwined with the reward processes of the human brain, which has evolved to appreciate the process of adaptability itself. However, whether we can claim that humour motivates action directly in modern humans or is instead a tool of cognitive development, we will examine shortly.

Either way, humour has played a previously overlooked role in the intellectual development of the species. Indeed, rather than a contributory factor, it is potentially one of the fundamental sources of the species' unparalleled cognitive capacity. Assumptions that, *vice versa*, humour is a consequent of our cognitive ability, a by-product of some other intellectual process necessary in our large and active brains, fail to explain the intense reward structure with which it has been endowed. Consequents exist because of antecedents, and require no evolutionary encouragement.

There is, of course, something missing from our hominoidal narrative above. Whether or not we decide to award him a humorous response (with or without laughter) for his sudden pattern recognition depends upon our speculation regarding the point at which humour first evolved. We have started with a hominoid here, implying that humour may not be restricted to homo sapiens, but have side-stepped the question of whether our hunter-gatherer experiences a humorous response for what we would now consider basic perceptual functionality. If we were to assume that he did, it might be reasonable to assume also that humour had only recently developed, since we now experience no such rewards *in adulthood* for exerting ourselves in a similar fashion. The potential points at which humour did, or does, exert its influence over the development of the individual or the species are debated further in *Phylogeny And The Recapitulative Question*.

There are various other alternatives here, though, one of which is that humour came about much earlier on the evolutionary scale, somewhere back along the mammalian line (which we'll examine more closely in *The Zoological Debate*), or only shortly before modern humans arrived about 130 000 to 100 000 years ago. There are a many, many other questions to be answered before we can even begin to speculate on this one, however, and many other species to be assessed.

The Development Of The External Signal; Laughter As A Method Of Data Transferral; Data Transferral And Sexual Selection

Just as reproduction necessarily existed before the development of the rewards with which we humans now associate it, so too humour existed before the humorous response with which it now appears intricately connected. In this context, then, humour refers to the surprise recognition of patterns, unrewarded and unspecialized, before the evolution of rewards that would massively increase the speed, efficiency and capacity of recognition. Attempts to argue the opposite, that laughter, while fulfilling its present function, preceded the existence of humour, are very difficult to entertain. How (and why) would laughter, with or without a social role of reassurance or genetic fitness, lead to internal cognitive processes, and to punning, to absurdity, to slapstick?

Evolution takes things one step at a time. Macro-development of complex systems does not occur, and each stage must confer a benefit on the individual organism for it to achieve success. Humour as a dry process pre-dated the overt signal we refer to as laughter, since otherwise there would have been nothing to laugh *at*, nothing to communicate through such a visible and audible external event. Communication is a method of data transferral, and only exists to communicate that information, not for its own ends. As a consequence, the individual must have found things amusing before he or she could communicate it to others, and it is this funniness, in isolation of communication, that is of paramount importance in this theory.

However, laughter did develop, and we can not overlook the role it plays. The humorous response, as we have said, is that which has spurred the expansion of cognitive ability, exerting a profound influence over the intellectual evolution of the species, and is fundamentally egocentric. Consequently, what role can we assign to laughter, and why should it exist? In simple terms laughter is an external sign of inner recognition, a usually involuntary expression to others that we are capable of discerning patterns in unlikely places. It is an external exaggeration of our internal rewards, communicating socially that something important, something valuable, is taking place beneath the surface. It provides us with an insight into the minds of others, communicating far more than the good intentions favoured by earlier theories – our mental aptitude, experience and perception – in short, a snapshot of all the information required to create the humorous response in the first place. Since it is founded in such fundamental cognitive processes its communication in an instant is a remarkable method of data transferral.

Such details would not otherwise be available without invasive, time-consuming and potentially confrontational enquiry or declaration. As a constantly whirring social research tool it runs quietly in the background while the rest of life receives our conscious attention. In the time it takes for a group to react to an individual's witticism, the individual will be able to assess and absorb extensive information about the present company. Comparative linguistic enquiry could takes minutes, if not hours, as well as honesty and self-knowledge, before such personal insights were disclosed, and the observer would have to be a skilled researcher and interlocutor. But with humour information is transmitted regardless of any *comedic competence* in the observer, since what has traditionally been considered *appreciation* of humour is a cognitive achievement worthy of declaration in itself.

The value awarded this declaration is undoubted and well documented but the reasons have been misunderstood. A *good* sense of humour is repeatedly considered one of the most important factors in mate selection, often ranking above physical attraction (Sprecher & Regan, 2002; Toro-Morn & Sprecher, 2003). This analysis of the potential mate's value is founded on the instinct that a person who can make you laugh has noticed patterns you have not yet recognized, with all the evolutionary benefits this entails regarding perception, cognitive capacity and adaptability. By laughing in return, the individual communicates that he or she has now recognized and appreciated those patterns, thereby giving assent to their validity. The traditional distinction between *producers* as individuals who manufacture instances of humour and *appreciators* who laugh in response is hence no longer quite as clear cut as it once was, since the same fundamental process of pattern recognition occurs in both parties, the one simply revealing those patterns to those who have not yet perceived them but who then do so when appropriately informed. The first party's advance recognition aside, there is consequently a complicity between the two, a similarity of perception.

It is perhaps the person who does not laugh in response who deserves a separate distinction, since he or she has either failed to be surprised by the pattern (and consequently provides no assent to its recognition since its declaration is considered to be of no value) or has failed to recognize the intended pattern at all. An individual falling into the former category may be considered amusing and sexually attractive, but not for the reasons other researchers have suggested. Here there has generally been a presumption that humour has evolved purely as an external indicator of genetic fitness through sexual selection. An amusing person may be more creatively able and, therefore, consequently possess a higher "mate value," relieving them of the pressure to laugh in "sexual signalling" (Kauffman et al, 2007). This is misleading. The sexual attraction which may or may not attach to such a person is founded on their ability to have become so familiar with patterns by which we are still surprised that they no longer react, hence communicating by their absence of mirth a depth of perception and experience we would consider a genetic asset. Their absence of laughter (whether genuine or acquired) is determined by the basic mechanism of humour, and does not represent the economical suspension of an overt form of sexual signalling.

Indeed, it is difficult to support a theory for the evolution of humour that does not award it a unique function. Physique and physical prowess already exist as indices of genetic fitness for mate selection, and the simple statement that females have favoured males who display humour fails to explain why that humour is so important, how its remarkable diversity has come about, or, indeed, the nature of its mechanism. Besides, humour occurs outside the sexual arena on a frequent basis without a competitive element, and unless we are to believe that this is training for later exploitation, such investment would be redundant.

The sexual dimorphism of laughter has also been well documented (Rucas et al, 2006; Buss, 1994; Kaufman et al, 2007), and although there are minor differences in MRI scans of male and female brains while experiencing a humorous response, there is little evidence to suggest that males actually find things less amusing than females (Reiss et al, 2005). The tendency of males to favour females who laugh at their humour, and for females to favour males who make them laugh, is likely to relate to issues of male dominance and female acquiescence in a natural environment requiring analysis and interpretation, and may reflect more specifically the role of the male in matters of spatial manipulation, whether hunting on behalf of or defending their mate, their offspring or their tribe. These instincts persist today, and the tendency for males to engage in *banter* performs two functions: the display of perceptual capacity to available females, and the declaration of prowess to competitors. The rhetorical and oratorical impact of wit is based on the same principles. Other researchers who have seen the *production* of humour as an index of genetic fitness (Bressler, 2005) have assumed that we are attracted to those who communicate it because it is metabolically expensive for them to do so, rather than because we are surprised by their perceptual capacity. There can be no stronger reflection of an individual's intellectual clarity than the sudden, revealing communication of a previously unrecognized but now accurately reproduced pattern.

We should not entirely overlook, however, the fact that the humorous response is an expensive process. Those who laugh are declaring that they have sufficient resources to do so, and those who laugh a lot are exhibiting an abundance that is likely to be interpreted as a good genetic bet. Hence females who laugh a great deal at a male's jokes are not only acquiescing to their perception of the world, they are advertising a rich supply of nutrients, along with vibrancy and good health, with which to raise potential offspring. Indeed, this boast of abundance reappears in the often artificial laughter sometimes associated with mockery as a simple communication of apparent superiority; a swift confirmation that the adversary is resourceful. Interestingly, the use of artificial laughter in such circumstances costs little or nothing, since no humorous response has actually occurred. Even when the humorous response in mockery is genuine, its function is still to intimidate by revealing that the mocker has recognized patterns about the victim the victim has not; an invasive, threatening communication that his or her life has been laid open to scrutiny and immediately apprehended in all its simplicity.

Why, then, is the external signal evidenced in the humorous response that which we recognize today as laughter? Certain elements of laughter reproduce those as seen in other positive declarations, such as smiling, and use a not dissimilar selection of muscles, and consequently it may have evolved by drawing on positive associations already apparent in the facial repertoire to communicate a moment of heightened pleasure in this fashion. Alternatively, it may have evolved from a completely separate call, which had perhaps with the development of more advanced linguistic systems become redundant. Either way it is likely to have originated in a much milder call, pressurized by sexual selection to become increasingly overt as both males and females chose mates who displayed it clearly.

Phylogeny And The Question
Of Recapitulation

Considering the remarkable cognitive and perceptual benefits of humour, when did, or does, it exert its influence over the development of the individual or the species? There are many questions to be answered here.

First, is humour still functional on an ontogenic level? Does it play an active role in the development of the individual's cognitive abilities in either infancy or adulthood, or is its presence entirely vestigial, a record of phylogeny, having produced its necessary effects of cognitive expansion perhaps hundreds of thousands or even millions of years ago? If the latter were true, we would possess a sense of humour now because the human brain became optimized for such perception in a manner that has benefited it evolutionarily, but after such cognitive development occurred the *humour instinct* remained with us, inactive regarding cognition in both infancy and adulthood but socially cohesive and culturally valuable, predisposing us to relish in the recognition of new patterns in different contexts. Its unconscious activity in evolutionary stages honed the human mind for conscious, explicit analysis and adaptability in its modern state.

On this basis our hominoid ancestor, or one at an indeterminate point preceding or succeeding him, would indeed have experienced a humorous response to reward his remarkable perceptions, which then amounted to little more than sudden, unconscious apprehension of entities in altered states. Further, there is no reason to presume that the action of humour was originally unconscious. By conferring rewards the process of humour encouraged cognitive application and development, which, stage by stage, could have increased in speed and efficiency until certain previously laboured, conscious and time-consuming perceptions and calculations gradually became so fast, and so quotidian, that they were transferred to the unconscious.

The intuitive response is to presume that humour is no longer active in adults, since it doesn't seem to *do* anything any more, yet the fact that it continues so actively throughout life (including beyond the ability to reproduce) I find difficult to reconcile with such an idea. We could perhaps surmise that humour in adulthood continues to encourage essential neuronal activity, a sort of cognitive maintenance, based around the important faculties of perception and information processing, and this is not beyond the realms of possibility, but evidence suggests that the absence of a sense of humour has little effect on cognitive ability. However, I am dissatisfied with the research conducted along these lines since it relies upon stipulations of *correct* and *incorrect* humour. Unfortunately, on this basis it is also impossible to reinterpret the available data in the light of this theory.

Modern human adults do not generally laugh at upside-down ducks, but as we saw in the hall of mirrors it requires only one step of disorientation to render us potentially hysterical at simple reflections. Consequently, it is also possible that humour is still an active cognitive tool as much as it ever was, and that human perception will continue to develop, transferring an increasing number of currently unfamiliar operations into the unconscious.

Further, although modern human adults do not generally laugh at upside-down ducks, modern human infants frequently do, which leads us to the question of whether humour is currently active in infantile cognitive development. Simply turning an infant's toy animal upside down and walking it along on its head is frequently performed by adults since it often leads to laughter in the infant. Earlier attempts to explain these responses by abstract notions of *incongruity* or *absurdity* (such as Pien & Rothbart, 1980) are far-fetched at best, and evolutionarily nonsensical.

However, the simultaneity of stages of cognitive development and the progress of humorous responses in infancy suggests that humour is a process by which the child is being encouraged to repeat or hone specific neuronal activity. In this context humour would constitute a form of programme establishing a scaffold of perceptual aptitude. To some extent that framework is encouraged by social interaction, but it seems likely that such fundamental cerebral development is largely innate, with education and interaction at these specifically important stages aiding, rather than causing, the infant's ability to recognize patterns. This individualistic view of cognitive development is at odds with much contemporary psychology with regards to higher social faculties, yet the fundamentally egocentric nature of humour appears incompatible with any other conclusion.

Is it possible, then, to trace the childhood development of humour and attempt to apply it to phylogeny with any meaningful implications regarding the development of language, of comprehension, of adaptability? What is noticeable during an attempt to do so is that the child appears to develop a working interaction with the basic principles of humour before language exists in any format requiring syntactical combination. The infant clearly laughs at humorous stimuli and is capable of initiating games intended to produce the humorous response for its own benefit before it is capable of dealing with the complexities of language. Once language is adopted, however, the process of linguistic humour, despite its mirroring of the earlier form, requires a relearning of the principles involved.

Is it plausible that the advanced pattern recognition involved in humour is necessary for linguistic comprehension or that its evolution was at least a contributory factor in humankind's facility with language, or that other associated faculties are accelerated by these cognitive processes in infancy? Newell and Simon have argued that expert knowledge such as playing chess or fluent speaking of a language requires the storage of fifty thousand patterns of similarity (Newell & Simon, 1972), yet it should be noted that the patterns to which they refer are unique for each new unit of information, rather then the generic and universally applicable versions of this theory. Corballis (1999) interprets work by the neuroscientist Rizzolatti as lending weight to the idea that reciprocity of gesture constituted a precursor to language, aided by the existence of so-called *mirror neurons* that fire when a monkey "observes somebody else, either a conspecific or a human experimenter, performing the same class of actions" (Iacoboni et al, 2005), which we might relate to the human infant's game of *clap hands*. Interestingly, such cells are located in an area of the monkey cortex "that appears to be homologous to Broca's area in the human brain, which is critically involved in the programming of human speech" (Corballis 1999). It seems unlikely that the basic formations of language, syntax and grammar, would be possible without facility with patterns of some variety. Alternatively, is the existence of pattern recognition a process of abstract apprehension that, without being specifically connected with the ability to think linguistically, heightened the ability to store representational articles and functions and consequently facilitated language's subsequent development?

"Human speech ability depends on two factors – specialized anatomy and a special-purpose 'functional language system' that regulates speech production, speech perception, and syntax in the human brain. Both anatomy and brain had to evolve from the primate base of the human-ape common ancestor to make human speech, language, thought, and culture possible."

(Lieberman, 1998)

To what degree could laughter's original role, then, be seen as a pre-lingual signal to communicate complicity and comprehension, arising before more complex systems had developed? Its ability to transfer large quantities of information swiftly as discussed above could have afforded it a relatively complex basis on which to gauge the views of others while formal language was still in its infancy. This proto-language of laughter would constitute the first adaptable, vocalized method of data transferral enabling subtle externalization of complex inner processes. Could we, on this basis, suggest that humans may first have exhibited an entirely internal, non-laughter-based form of humour, followed by a laughter-based version before syntax evolved, leading finally, in modern humans, to a language-based form of humour that has to be re-absorbed into the now innate earlier stages of the process?

We may also consider for a moment the different natures of the two stages of humour acquisition in infancy. I have suggested that the first phase of development is largely innate, and indeed, without language with which to educate the infant it would be difficult to imagine exactly how such a complex system could be entirely socially induced. The difficulty experienced by children when readapting their humorous ability to language invites a glimpse of the complexity of the perceptual system involved. We have also presumed that the fundamental nature of the associated cognition makes it highly unlikely to be learnt, yet we appear to have a later, language-based stage that requires application and genuine acquisition. I suggest we are dealing with little more than the cultural and language-specific application of a faculty that is as innate and instinctive as the ability for linguistic thought itself, which still requires the acquisition of a specific language.

Indeed, the format of jokes and witticisms is very much dependent upon cultural expectations.

Furthermore, could the first forms of humour have consisted of surprising entity completion, as they clearly do in the childhood linguistic developmental stage? A partially occluded object, for example, being suddenly recognized for what it is, would fulfil a similar environmental role to its linguistic counterpart. There are sound reasons for presuming this form of entity completion was a fore-runner phylogenically to what we now consider humour, since, as we have already stated, we can only recognize a pattern if we can first apprehend its constituent elements.

Revising Assumptions About Humour's Social And Communicative Roles

This theory states that humour is an internal process, not primarily intended for communication, but for cognitive development. It has, later, developed an external signal which enables that ability to be advertised in a usually involuntary and consequently honest manner. The existence of a social aspect to humour, and even the potential for laughter to be contagious, does not necessarily imply, as has been presumed by many theorists, that humour's principal function is social. Humour itself is egocentric, and the existence of laughter signifies nothing more than the declaration of the internal process. Its potentially contagious aspect reminds us to what degree the individual mind aspires to the achievement of pattern recognition, and the importance we presume other members of the species will award its correct functioning in either mate or peer selection.

Concentration on the overt signals of humour as the mainstay of research has compounded this distortion of the subject, whereby laughter has been seen to become the reason for the existence of humour itself. There is no denying, of course, that laughter has a developed social function, and it may even have played an important role as a form of proto-language, but its communicative element exists solely to communicate what has occurred in the mechanism of humour, the detail that has been perceived, and the information that perception has gleaned. The fact that communication often takes place during instances of humour does not automatically imply that communication is its principal function, since nearly all human functions involve some level of communication.

The humorous response consists of many other elements, expensive ones, that are not necessary to produce laughter, and which must by themselves be explained. There is little evolutionary justification for investment in internal congratulation if humour is essentially social. Any sign of reassurance, such as a smile, would fulfil the same function just as well. Besides, almost all emotions find some form of external expression, especially in the face. It is beneficial generally to the species to wear its heart on its sleeve; for cohesion, for altruism, for comprehension, yet we would not, I take it, claim that the purpose of all emotions is primarily social simply because they feature their own method of communication. Indeed, just as physique and physical prowess provide extant and successful indices for genetic fitness that make it unlikely that humour evolved to play an identical, duplicate role in social interaction, so too do other forms of social activity (such as music and dance) provide mechanisms and signals of social cohesion and tribal affirmation that would render it extraneous in these alternative arenas also. Further, any assertion that the reason for humour's existence is to produce laughter does nothing to explain its rich diversity and complexity.

Research such as Provine's[6], stating that people laugh more frequently in the company of others than when alone (Provine & Fischer, 1989) is generally interpreted as proof of laughter's social function. However, it is usually also taken to confirm that humour is therefore necessarily social in nature as well, yet knowledge of the mechanism implies there should be no difference in its basic functionality whether the individual is in the presence of others or not. There are various reasons for the discrepancy.

First, it is necessary to split the mechanism and the function of humour from the outward signal of laughter, just as we must split the outward signal of laughter from the remainder of the humorous

---

[6] Provine's work, although laudable, is at odds with much of my theory due to our entirely different starting points: Provine set out to explain laughter, whereas I set out to explain humour, the thing that produces that laughter. Consequently I find Provine has made assumptions about the stimulus that have affected his interpretation of its rewards, and his association of laughter with the entirety of the humorous response has led to misconceptions about the social nature of humour itself.

response. Does the individual find things less funny when in isolation, do they find things funny less often, or do they simply laugh less while finding things just as funny, just as frequently, as when in company? Even removing the supposed verisimilitude of social interaction involved in the reading of a book or the watching of a television show, I am unwilling to accept from empirical evidence that humour is less active or effective in circumstances of reduced social stimuli, but there are very reasonable grounds for expecting it to be less frequent and sometimes less overtly expressed.

The presence of another initiates the incursion of their worldview on our own. In isolation, it is uncommon to be surprised by the environment around us (although not impossible) since the majority of our interpretations will continue to hold true unless our attention is drawn to them, either by the occurrence of a major event or the actions of another animate being. This does, not, however, imply that either the mechanism or the function of humour is impaired by solitude, but that our most frequent exposure to assumptions and assessments that are likely to surprise us is in the company of others, where we can marvel all the more readily at how an individual of our species, with exposure to the same stimuli, the same language and the same world, can differ so wildly in their perceptions.

Clearly, however, humour often exists in social formats. The human species turns basic functions and impluses that exist in the individual, and, indeed, in other species, into group events (such as sport for the hunt, music and dance for the mating or territory call) and the arena of formal *comedy* is a socially organized form of humour, taking the innate, internal process and externalizing it to reinforce all the normal bonds as evidenced in other social and tribal events. However, to say that comedy is the reason for the existence of humour would be akin to stating that sport is the reason for the existence of the hunt; a simple confusion of application with function, and this resonates throughout many of the classic misinterpretations of its role. The external process of humour can be employed as an anti-dominance weapon, just as it can be used as a romantic seduction or a social cement, a form of political persuasion or emotional corrective, but these explain neither its function nor its mechanism, each describing only a proportion of the situations in which it arises. These are merely applications, not functions, just as a physically beautiful person may *use* their beauty to gain preferment elsewhere in life beyond the attraction of a mate, and the fact that other strategies can be employed instead of humour in any of these situations weakens any evolutionary argument for its development for that purpose.

The overt expression of laughter does indeed appear to be exaggerated in company, however (Provine, 2000), and claims for the social role of humour are often supported by the idea that laughter is contagious. Humans want to laugh, of course, because it is a reward for cognition. They also want to show themselves to be clever, and it is quite possible that the sight of others laughing may predispose us to laughter ourselves, since we are being told there is a pattern available to be recognized. It would expose us as witless indeed if everyone else had perceived something that we had missed, and consequently the mind is keen to ensure that we are not isolated by the remaining members of a cleverer, more perceptive society. Further, the existence of *rapid involuntary facial mimicry* in both humans and non-humans (Meltzoff & Moore, 1977) encourages the adoption of another's responses in all cases of communication, not merely laughter. It is also conceivable that instances of laughter themselves may form their own pattern, which, if surprising to the individual, could result in the evocation of a humorous response.

It would, consequently, seem perfectly reasonable for there to be some minor alteration in the nature of laughter in social groups, but not in the inner humorous response, which should remain unaltered. However, the existence of laughter may well alert us to patterns we may not have recognized if left to our own devices, since those around us provide a naturally occurring version of *assisted recognition*. Also, humour helps to explain to others that we have understood the patterns to which they refer, and is hence invaluable in the process of selecting and deselecting those who are fit for the task at hand. Keenness or reluctance to laugh at certain subjects almost certainly provides an exaggeration or attenuation of the response (the physiological basis of the humorous response features both voluntary and involuntary networks: Wild et al, 2003) dependent upon the degree to which the individual wishes to advertise their recognition of the pattern. In this manner we observe the exaggerated guffaws associated with jokes about sex and the more nervous, tentative responses sometimes produced by humour about aggression. However, in certain circumstances the fact that either subject is being commented on in public may be found surprising, increasing the humorous response.

Indeed, the desire to be able to laugh at what other people are laughing at is so strong that children dedicate themselves to mastering the joke format in order that they too can find it amusing. Despite the fact that they are already capable of laughter and humorous responses, the child invests time and effort in prospective comprehension, corrected as they go along by the parental unit. If social affirmation were the function of the joke the infant could laugh anyway, whether they had understood it or not, yet they do not, since the motivation for working at the format is neither the reward of laughter nor the communication with peers, but the ability to perceive the patterns others have recognized. At this stage of development, humour is being viewed by the mind as a measure of its own cognitive ability, and the child is failing. Suggestions that the child's motivation is to furnish it with a new form of creativity, that it desires to produce jokes itself, are denied by normal behaviour subsequent to the acquisition of linguistic humour, since cessation of joke production is usual, having been regular and frequent (although inept) during the process of prospective comprehension.

Contagious laughter, except in instances of obvious dysfunction, is consequently founded in an assessment, whereby the balance of opinion is gauged and the individual decides whether he or she is likely to gain or lose by laughing or by exaggerating or attenuating their responses. As my field research is currently suggesting, laughing while outnumbered by those who are not laughing very rarely leads to their adoption of it; frequently, indeed, it leads to irritation and suspicion. This process by which the individual assesses the likelihood of correctness in the patterns being acknowledged by the group based upon the balance of opinion will exhibit itself to varying degrees depending upon his or her personality.

Provine's laughter box (Provine, 1992), cited as evidence that laughter is contagious without any further stimulus, is surely flawed. The reduction of laughter evoked each time it repeated implies there was genuine humour occurring in the class, not automatic, laughter-induced laughter, else why should the responses of the students have diminished? Provine is not claiming, surely, that these individuals became *immune* to the contagion, and now do not laugh at laughter at all. The lessening of the response is in accordance with that which we would expect for the normal reaction to a humorous stimulus, implying that there was something actually *funny* about the event[7], a single instance of humour that wore thin, not pure laughter itself, which should remain consistently contagious if we are to accept it as such at all.

---

[7] I am unaware of the details of the box and was not present during the research, so I can only surmise, but it is common for the reproduction (repetition) of a human faculty or characteristic, such as speech or other expressions, to be found amusing if it is presented in a surprising manner. This is simple translational mapping, in this case on an auditory basis.

Laughter In Peer Groups

Due to the nature of patterns being founded in repetition, familiarity is to some degree a potential facilitator of humour, although this familiarity must not deny our ability to be surprised by the process of recognition.

Criticisms by researchers such as Provine that the vast majority of what makes friends laugh amongst themselves is not funny is caused by a misinterpretation of the mechanism of humour (Provine, 1996). Provine claims only "ten to twenty" per cent of the episodes recorded during his field research could be classed as humorous, although the approximation of his figures reveals the uncertainty of his terms:

"The frequent laughter heard at crowded social gatherings is not due to a furious rate of joke-telling by guests. Most pre-laugh dialogue is like that of an interminable television situation comedy scripted by an extremely ungifted writer."

Beneath the pejorative nature of Provine's assessment lie assumptions about the existence of *good* or *bad* humour that are still widespread, contributing to the paucity of comprehension of the humorous mechanism. Provine has incorrectly assumed that many of the stimuli that produced laughter in his field research were in fact not instances of humour at all. Granted, to an outsider the humour within a group can often seem repetitive, but to dismiss this as humourless is to have misunderstood the concept of the *in* or *running* joke, frames of reference, meta-meaning and pattern resurgence. Indeed, humour in peer groups is much more than just peer recognition or reassurance. Provine's list of weak attempts at humour reproduces only the linguistic elements as his team witnessed them; it does not communicate all the other aspects of humour, media and cross-media patterns and references surrounding them. Even apparently simple statements can be overlaid with constantly developing and shifting ulterior meanings and references (especially so, in fact, among individuals with frequent and intense exposure to each other), enabling the supposed repetition of an event to achieve fresh vigour in its delivery, maintaining, for a while, our surprise. I also suspect Provine caused himself a few unnecessary problems by conducting his research on college students, whose popular cultural references may have eluded him.

Provine goes on to say that many instances of laughter occurred, in the absence of attempts at humour, on greeting or leaving a peer. I am currently conducting some field research on this matter, and although it is as yet incomplete, I have been unable to identify a single instance of the salutatory laughter suggested by Provine. This is understandable, however, since my analysis is based upon a definition of humour unavailable to Provine, who had to make assumptions about what could and could not be classed as humour without a working knowledge of its mechanism.

It is necessary to move on from the assumption that *involuntary* laughter is produced among friends out of altruism directed towards each other's witticisms, since such a phenomenon is inconsistent with both the mechanism and the function of humour. We must take care, however, not to overlook fake or *voluntary* laughter, which we have no reason to presume will occur any less frequently than the fake compliment, or indeed the fake orgasm. Fakery involved in laughter, however, does not award it some specialized social function peculiar to itself, and, just as the fake orgasm does not explain the presence of the genuine article, nor does the social aspect of fake laughter explain the origins of the existence of humour. The purpose of language, we presume, is not to facilitate lying. Whether for the purposes of social harmony or self-preservation, implied recognition or affected surprise at patterns of which we are already fully aware is a simple enough social artifice akin to listening attentively to a boring story. The putative honesty of the signal of humour is decidedly questionable, and this has in itself caused problems with the interpretation of data over the years.

Suppression And Denial: Socialization And The Acquisition Of The Altruistic Impulse

The mechanism and function as described thus far obtain in all instances during which humour occurs. However, there are situations in which the mechanism of humour is sometimes over-ridden, either by acquired suppression or by contrary neurological activity.

The most common example of the denial of humour occurs during the acknowledgement of another's pain. However, although this suppression is widespread it is in no way universal. The tendency for children to laugh at each other's misfortune implies that the absence of humour in similar, supposedly inappropriate situations in adult life is the result of suppression, learnt by socialization as the individual begins to think altruistically and to conform to expectations. There are many individual and personal reasons for these restrictions on laughter, but none of them relates to the mechanism of humour itself. They are, instead, a curtailing of the process, brought about by learnt concerns about its potential repercussions.

However, this does *not* mean that humour has necessarily to be friendly, conciliatory, inconsequential or comprised of any other stipulated quality by which we can erroneously claim that certain things are funny and others not. It does mean, however, that humour may be denied, or suppressed, if the circumstances of the individual psyche dictate that it should be. In different individuals, their very different and individual senses of humour will be over-ridden for different reasons; some with great regularity, and others barely at all. Although humour is largely involuntary, it is possible to acquire behaviour (as comedians do) which suppresses the arousal of the humorous response. The acquisition of altruistic suppression is not dissimilar but is learnt over a number of years from experience and education. The success of the altruistic impulse lies in the mutuality of its nature, and those who depart from what we would expect are often viewed as amoral or socially harmful. The momentary cognitive reward of humour is generally considered less important than potentially life-supporting altruism, and those who fail to suppress it are sometimes viewed as selfish and unthoughtful. The altruistic impulse is well documented in relation to other human activity (Gavanescul, 1895) and indeed non-human activity (de Waal, 2008).

There are also psychological states capable of producing an unresponsiveness or aversion to stimuli when the individual may claim to be *not in the mood*. Threatening, stressful or otherwise challenging situations may lead to a tendency to deny humour. Over-excitability is a potential drawback of humour since it averts our attention from the immediate circumstances, and the benefits of curtailing emotional arousal in threatening situations are clear. The enforced gravity calms the reward structure and prevents it from becoming associated with potentially damaging situations. Later, however, once the circumstances have changed, we may laugh at the event in retrospect since there is no longer any sound judgemental reason for denying its activity.

Humour is not an emotion, although it does produce an emotional response. Its activity encourages cognitive development, not similar behaviour as happiness does, and it can consequently lead to a conflict between cortical activity and emotional motivation. At such times humour is often considered inappropriate and is potentially denied.

Implications

The Zoological Debate

What new light does *pattern recognition theory* throw on the ancient debate regarding the possible existence of humour in analogous forms or to lesser extents in other species? No other fundamental evolutionary impulse is exhibited solely by humans. Sexual gratification, anger, jealousy, love for mates and young, the desire to nest and build and every other motivational instinct that arises in humans arises elsewhere in the animal kingdom.[8] Since the cognitive processes involved in humour are fundamental to speed of perception, it is possible, then, that milder versions of the same mechanism exist in all mammalian brains, or even further afield, performing identical cognitive functions without the same hilarity of expression. Yet humankind *is* extraordinarily different from other animals intellectually, which leads us to the proposition that humour was instrumental in the cognitive evolution of the species and perhaps therefore restricted to it.

---

[8] Humour, again, is not merely an exaggeration of happiness as some have presumed, since it plays a very different role and is stimulated by different impulses.

However, research on the issue has been hampered by assumptions regarding the nature of humour and the importance of laughter. The presumption that tickling is a humorous stimulus has led to a large amount of confusing data and misleading literature. Initially it spawned mock-aggression theories which do not stand up to scrutiny even regarding tickling itself, since only certain parts of the body generally respond to such stimulation. Play attack of other forms, such as ruffling a person's hair repeatedly or tickling a person's forehead, very rarely leads to laughter, yet the elements of aggression in jest remain. Further, humorous stimuli don't have to be delivered in a declarative *in jest* manner for them to be funny. Most individuals have experienced serious films they consider to be unintentionally funny, and any stimulus can prove so regardless of whether it has been prepared for our consumption or not. It is inescapable that involuntary responses to tickling are based upon a certain physical sensitivity unrelated to the action of the game, otherwise patients who have lost all sensitivity through paralysis should continue to laugh during tickling as long as they can see the source of the stimulus, and there is no evidence to support this. Indeed, the fact that, as Harris and Christenfeld have shown, the stimulus need not be human, or even natural, reduces the experience to a purely sensory, egocentric affair not dependent upon intrapersonal relationships (Harris & Christenfeld, 1999).

Also contrary to the principles of mock-aggression theories, the content of humour need not contain any human or social element, and the vast majority of instances of humour bear no relation to aggression or aggressive play. How, for example, would such a theory explain the development of humorous peculiarities such as punning, especially when based around two inanimate objects? Attempts to explain modern humour by declaring it a faculty that has altered in nature with the evolution of the species, gradually departing from its original function and mechanism for some unidentified reason, leave us requiring a whole new theory of how and why it functions as it does *now*, and we are back to square one.

Indeed, although it is a very attractive idea to prove the existence of humour in other species, I would be the first to state that laughter as a result of tickling is inconclusive evidence, disagreeing entirely as I do with Provine's statement that "tickling is essential to understanding the associated social vocalization of laughter" (Provine, 2000). As Provine makes clear, the laughter produced by chimpanzees is different from human laughter, constituting as it does a "breathy pant-like sound."[9] Determining the causal link between humour and laughter in tickling, especially in other species, is a major problem. The fact that many people dislike tickling is impossible to reconcile with its putative relation to the fundamental mechanism of the humorous response. Provine's excellent research reveals that it doesn't produce laughter in all people either (84% of those being tickled claim to laugh, as opposed to 80% of those doing the tickling) yet at no point has he asked the simple question of *Are you finding this funny?* Again, neither is it possible to claim that those who dislike being tickled are the ones who don't laugh. If it were so, we could propose that this sort of humour just isn't to everybody's taste, but in fact many people who do not enjoy the process, nor find it in the slightest bit amusing, still find themselves producing the usual involuntary response associated with being tickled. In humour, laughter is a fundamentally enjoyable response, whereas the effect of being tickled, despite its explosive and convulsive nature, was rated only *moderately pleasurable* (5.0 on a scale of 1.0 to 10.0, falling below the middle value of 5.5), with many people finding a proportion of its physiological effects unpleasant. Harris also concluded that "tickling does not lead to the same internal state of amusement as does comedy. Just as crying while cutting an onion has little in common with crying at a funeral, so the states associated with the two types of laughter may be fundamentally different." (Harris, 1999). Further, laughter evoked by *peek-a-boo* in infants tends to precede that caused by tickling by about two months, denying the theory that humorous laughter develops out of ticklish laughter.

The attraction of tickling for those who enjoy it is rooted in many things - in sexual foreplay, in affectionate proximity, in bonding, in pleasurable physical stimulation – all elements that may contribute to a state of happiness, but not, in isolation, to humour. However, there does appear to be a method to good tickling that is indeed grounded in the fundamental principles of *pattern recognition theory*, potentially compounding the effect of the sensory stimulation with an element of humour. Tickling of infants by their parents tends to adopt a similar format to *peek-a-boo*, which also exists to some degree in the adult version as I have witnessed it. The tickler is effectively telling a joke in

---

[9] I have been unable to conduct any sonic experiments thus far but I am keen to confirm or deny the similarity of the response produced by tickling to that produced by humorous stimuli in both infant and adult humans. Observation informs me that the former is different in timbre, force and regularity which may point further to its dissociation from the humorous response.

this interpretation, and the existence of *rapid involuntary facial mimicry* and the general contagion of all emotions would account for their reciprocal laughter. It is probable that tickling is therefore partly humorous, initiating a response which is then exaggerated by involuntary convulsion aroused by defence mechanisms, producing the full gamut of qualitative experiences associated with the process as we know it.

However, *pattern recognition theory* now suggests ways in which we might begin to analyse whether humour is present in chimpanzees, replicating non-tactile human infantile pattern recognition games that are separate from, and unpolluted by, the inconclusive debate regarding tickling. First, do *peek-a-boo, clap hands, face pulling* or *tower demolition* elicit laughter in chimpanzees, or does any primate exhibit its own equivalent game or games? There are problems associated with this research, of course, since three of the games mentioned above can be difficult to perform without arousing fear. Humour is an individual process, and it is hard enough to predict whether a human being will laugh on cue, let alone a primate that does not share our language, our perceptions, our physiological processes or our experiences. If primates do not appear to exhibit similar games, close analysis of instances of laughter may reveal popular and regularly occurring processes of an analogous nature. Should the human infantile games fail to produce a response, exposure to alternative, more sensorily invasive patterns utilizing processes apparent in the natural environment of the primate should be attempted. Again, however, researchers must escape the notion that any excited call produced by a chimpanzee during sport or ambush is a form of laughter. The similarity of calls in group play to those given during ambush (despite their lower levels) imply they are perhaps nothing more than a prefiguration, anticipating the atmosphere of the real event in sport. We would not interpret the sound of a human mob as it riots as laughter, and we must take care not to make further incorrect presumptions based on outdated and unsupportable mock-aggression theories about chimpanzees and other primate species.

Chimpanzees, of course, are gregarious animals with complex social relationships based upon identity and recognition, but humour, as we have stated, is fundamentally egocentric. Even more solitary primates such as orang-utans appear to produce facial expressions considered to be homologous to human laughter (van Hooff & Preuschoft, 2003), yet without a knowledge of the mechanism of humour it has not been possible to conclude whether such expressions are homologous in function and representative of homologous mechanisms. *Pattern recognition theory* in combination with MRI will enable a more accurate estimation of humour in other species by clarifying the nature of appropriate experiments designed to evoke a humorous response. If research confirms the existence of humour in chimpanzees, similar experiments would be possible on species who do not (apparently) exhibit an overt signal of humour, such as cats, by employing similar stimuli to those successfully evocative in chimpanzees and comparing MRI results.

There are, however, potential obstacles to the existence of humour in lower mammalian orders, and even in other primates, and I am not optimistic about the probability of confirmative results. The human mind has developed a logical framework by which we swiftly sort sensory data into hierarchies of entities and qualities as we effortlessly analyse our environment. We have a heightened sense of units, of patterns, and of complex interactions. Most of all, though, we have language – a great facilitator of humour, and the method by which a fair proportion of it is passed from one individual to another. If we see humour as much more than a swift perceptual system, actively encouraging and enabling our adaptability to different circumstances, it is worth considering that most mammals are not, in fact, actively adaptable. Adaptability in itself, when occurring at the level of the conscious individual, requires a certain ability to think in an abstract nature, since functions must be separated from their objects and reapplied, or recognized, elsewhere.

As a small glint of hope to those who are keen to find humour in other species, however, it may be no coincidence that certain primates, apes and monkeys appear to laugh while also being the most cognitively able of animals, and the species that laughs most outside humankind is the chimpanzee, which also exhibits the greatest adaptability and task-solving ability. Perhaps they, too, have benefited from humour during their evolution.

Artificial Intelligence

Knowledge of the mechanism of humour brings us one step closer to the production of an artificial being that exhibits genuine individuality. The absence of humour from machines has contributed a great deal towards their robotic reputation: since a sense of humour is so important to us in everything from the entertainment we choose to our selection of both mates and peers, our perception of the humourless is that it is decidedly inhuman. Colleagues or teachers or other individuals who display no sense of humour are viewed as lifeless and often disparaged as robots. Worse, our failure to comprehend its nature for so long has led to bizarre notions that, along with other faculties such as the appreciation of music or the production of poetry, it is part of the human *soul*, a supposedly defining aspect of human uniqueness that could never be reproduced in a machine.

The chance to prove otherwise is tantalizing, and I intend to develop a model by which the mechanism of humour could be incorporated into an artificial intelligence engine. It may be a very long time, admittedly, until we have developed hardware that will be able to support the functionality of the full model, but this is no longer because of our ignorance of humour. Rather, it is because of the difficulties inherent in AI associated with parallel processing of vast numbers of variables, with cross-media sensory data analysis, with the absorption, accumulation and recall of experience in a manner homologous to that of human memory and with the artificiality of reward structures within such systems.

There are then further difficulties to be addressed, such as the assessment of probabilities inherent in humour and the necessity of quantifying surprise in the face of potentially limitless associations and cross-references. This raises the problem of producing a truly learning computer that would start its life in a virgin state of innate processes but without knowledge, since we would not wish to affect its judgement by supplying it with information, with instructions for surprise, artificially. To do so would be to present it with a static interpretation of the world dependent on averages and supposedly objective data. This is fundamentally incompatible with the processes of reassessment that occur in humour due to habituation and neglect and would deny the basic ingredient of individuality so cherished by developers, although it is conceivable that default values could be programmed which would then be open to reassessment with experience. However, the limitless potential of association and the necessity of the being to possess excellent generalization abilities in its approach to categorization and analysis would render the programming of such probabilities a limited and problematic affair. The importance of meta-meaning and *unprovoked completion* in humour would also cause significant stumbling blocks. The faculty of pattern analysis would need to exist as a single network accessed by data received from any source in order to enable cross-media pattern recognition, and the flow of information through this channel would in itself present a significant challenge.

The AI problems regarding the potential for learning machines are well known. How can a static computer learn the content and the patterns of the world as humans do? Humans are locomotive, exploratory animals that hone their perceptions and responses by direct interaction with the physical world in the form of manipulation, and whose humour is based fundamentally on their orientation, both physically and metaphorically. However, the potential for testing exists in much more basic formats, and I intend to produce a working model restricted to the recognition of non-verbal linguistic humour. Although unable to originate humour due to its innate idleness the programme would display reactions to input, attempting to identify whether the information inputted was intended in a humorous manner or not.

The potential applications, even of a basic, unisensory or purely linguistic model, are extensive. *Humour* will feature a diagrammatic representation of the variables involved in the mechanism and their interaction. We may well still be a long way off, but we now at least know what lies ahead.

Analysis Of Dysfunction In Neurology And Psychology

"Is humour a kind or perception or is humour 'something' that is produced? Or is it both? The reluctance of neuroscientists to enter such inchoate fields is understandable…Although operational definitions of 'laughter,' 'humour' and 'funny' have been formulated for individual studies, a broad consensus on their exact meanings has yet to be reached. This is not a trivial handicap; it is obvious that what one means by humour and laughter will influence what kinds of experiments one designs for their analysis."

(Wild et al, 2003)

The neurological and psychological study of patients with certain dysfunctional conditions has been retarded by incorrect assertions regarding the mechanism, and to some degree the function, of humour. Clearer comprehension provided by this theory should facilitate more accurate interpretation of cranial activity under MRI and guide the production of more appropriate and effective experiments.

However, despite our knowledge of the mechanism of humour, what its discovery hasn't done for us is to reveal a set of criteria by which humour must occur in every patient. It is an endlessly individual faculty, and to that extent the neuroscientist is not as well off as they might have hoped to be by its explanation. However, a sound knowledge of the constituent elements by which an individual may potentially experience humour will have clarified some of the issues involved.

Psychometric testing, as a diagnostic or exploratory tool, involving experiments designed to assess the ability of patients with brain injuries to *comprehend* humour, have been misleading in their emphases and potentially unsound in their implications. The process of the recognition of patterns is necessarily dependent upon the individual, and consequently notions of *comprehending* or *decoding* instances of humour are flawed. Instead, the presentation of such tests identifies only the ability of the patient to identify the *intentions* of the originator of the humour, or even worse, the interpretations of the humour by the researcher, which, even if supported by a consensus of all those patients tested, points only to the ability of the subject to identify the cultural (and perhaps linguistic) interests of the society in question, not to a *comprehension of humour*. What is under analysis is effectively the patient's ability to empathize, not the ability to recognize and be surprised by patterns. The identification of the culturally expected norm is awarded a positive mark, yet failure to do so does not, in any way, prevent the patient from identifying humour elsewhere in the stimulus with good reason and a sound humorous mechanism. Its difference from the suggested cultural norm need have no basis in the incorrect functioning of humour, and further analysis will be required to identify potential damage to other cognitive or emotional functions.

Indeed, the concentration on linguistic (as opposed to non-formatted verbal) or cartoon humour in these circumstances, both of which are representational and require a certain grasp of cultural expectations (especially so in the case of linguistic humour which is, as we have seen, acquired by education and correction) is a further matter for concern. A fair proportion of modern comedy also frequently confounds the sort of intentions traditionally considered *correct* within such sources, yet is still found amusing. Indeed, a pre-joke child would be unable to complete the linguistic examples of these tests in the manner viewed as correct, yet they have fully functioning cognition and the ability to be amused by humour. If the anomalous subjects have found their interpretations amusing, then humour has taken place, and they have comprehended its mechanism, rather than our culturally-determined expressions of it, just as well as the psychologist. In many cases it may prove that better designed experiments yield generally the same results when returning to cases already researched, yet there are many concomitant issues which will inevitably have been overlooked, and which will undoubtedly expand our understanding of humour's physiological basis and its wider relation to other faculties.

There are further weaknesses in such testing, especially in the dichotomy assumed between *production* and *appreciation*, which are no longer adequate as descriptions. The assessment of *appreciation* is especially flawed, since the individual may identify more sources of humour in a stimulus than the psychologist has. This would not mean, as currently assumed, that the individual has appreciated the stimulus to a greater extent than those displaying lesser reactions, since the source of this reaction is in fact different in nature, regardless of the presentation of identical material. It is not inconceivable that what is perceived as the salient source of humour is dependent upon sexually dimorphic attitudes and facilities, in turn contributing to some degree towards the slight differences in humorous response exhibited by males and females in some MRI research (Reiss et al, 2005).

In the absence of *objective humour* the study of such patients is best undertaken according to their own direction. The identification of material the patient claims to find amusing, followed by their own analysis of it, will reveal a much more accurate picture of their ability to *comprehend* humour. Indeed, studies that have reported a disturbance of the ability to "perceive" humour due to "inappropriate focus on irrelevant detail," "egocentricity" or "paranoid attitude" (Ferguson et al, 1969) have misunderstood the nature of humour entirely, and consequently, perhaps, the nature of the patient's illness. However, whether the humorous process could be deemed fully functioning in many of these cases or not, the perception of patterns within the culturally expected norms is *probably* of sound evolutionary benefit to the individual, and to that degree, whatever has disturbed the ability to identify society's intentions and expectations could indeed be said to be dysfunctional. As such the traditional interpretations of disturbance of perception as symptoms of illness are potentially, but not necessarily, still correct.

Elsewhere, to what degree does an absence of humour (as opposed to an absence of laughter) relate to cognitive impairment? This may help us to establish to what degree humour is still functional regarding infantile and adult cognitive development. Unfortunately, large amounts of research conducted so far are not reinterpretable due to the stipulations of *correct* humour imposed at the time which may have overlooked its present and correct functioning. The establishment of any relationship between these factors may well, in turn, have diagnostic or remedial applications.

Pattern recognition theory may also shed light on various syndromes in mental health. In hypomania, for example, during an intensely creative phase of bipolar disorder the patient may feel an uncontrollable impulse to laugh at things he or she does not normally find funny (Akiskal, 2000). Is it coincidental that heightened creativity occurs at the same time, and is it possible to speculate, therefore, that the patient is identifying patterns where they would not normally recognize them? Earlier interpretations of humour would have presumed that this laughter was pathological and founded in the malfunctioning caused by the bipolar condition since what was not previously funny has suddenly become so, and, indeed, its causes could still originate in a heightened tendency to surprise caused by chemically increased neuronal activity rather than recognition. Yet the nature of pattern recognition enables the location of different humorous sources within the same stimulus. The typical inability of individuals to identify at what they are actually laughing (else we should all have understood the basis of humour all along) presents the distinct possibility that they are in fact laughing at different patterns previously unrecognized.

This theory will not, unfortunately, suddenly facilitate the discovery of remedial treatments for neurological or psychological illnesses, but it will, with careful application, remove some of the mysteries associated with humour that have led to potential misdiagnosis in various conditions and that have produced uncertainty regarding the direction neuroscientific research should most beneficially take. The patient must be assessed by different criteria, whether diagnosing dysfunction or scanning the brain to identify the neural correlates of humour, in order to gain a more accurate picture of its neurological and psychological foundation.

Conclusion

This theory has implications and ramifications in many subjects I have not been able to address here, and although proponents will generally hope to have presented their case as comprehensively as possible, I also hope I have only begun to scratch the surface.

From the starting point of the *lowest common denominator* in information processing it has developed older incongruity theories by identifying a precise mechanism that applies to any instance of humour. It then presents a justifiable evolutionary function lacking from previous interpretations, and posits humour as a major faculty in the human cognitive arsenal. It suggests much about the importance that faculty has played in the unique intellectual capacity of human beings, with potential contributions towards the linguistic faculty and the capacity for abstract thought. It goes on to demystify the nature and purpose of humorous games in infantile development and the impulse to induce laughter experienced by parents and guardians, and clarifies the role of laughter in social interaction. It explains the importance of humour in mate and peer selection and revises our prior assumptions to locate its operation squarely on an egocentric basis. It suggests methods by which we may clarify the potential for humour in other animals and proposes alterations to the methodology employed in psychometric testing as well as highlighting its relevance to neuroscientific research. It also promises to offer a model by which its mechanism of humour could be incorporated into artificial intelligence engines of the current or near future.

But this objective, global theory of humour does not stipulate what it is that we find funny, only how and why. We can not claim to be able to analyse patterns as if they were inherent within the stimulus in order to brand certain things funnier than others, since the process of surprise pattern recognition is dependent upon innumerable individual variables, and is consequently entirely subjective. Quantifying surprise is enormously difficult, and the impossibility of determining the many meta-meanings and associations the individual acquires through experience renders humour a very personal response indeed.

If humour is finding something funny, then it is the same process in all instances, regardless of whether everyone, or only one, is laughing. The different manifestations are cultural and individual, but the mechanism, and the function, remain the same.

Appendices

Bibliography

Aitchison, J. 2000. *The Seeds of Speech: Language Origin and Evolution*. Cambridge: Cambridge University Press.

Akiskal, H. 2000. Re-evaluating the prevalence of and diagnostic composition within the broad clinical spectrum of bipolar disorders. *Journal of Affective Disorders, vol. 59*, S5 - S30.

Appleton, B. 1997. Patterns and Software: Essential Concepts and Terminology. *Object Magazine Online, vol. 3, no. 5*.

Apte, M. L. 1985. *Humor and Laughter: An Anthropological Approach*. Ithaca: Cornell University Press.

Attardo, S. 1994. *Linguistic Theories of Humor*. New York: Mouton de Gruyter.

Attenborough, D. 1971. *A Blank on the Map*. ABC/BBC Colour Co-production.

Attenborough, D. 1980. *Life on Earth*. London: Book Club Associates.

Babad, E. 1974. A multi-method approach to the assessment of humor: A critical look at humor tests. *Journal of Personality, 42*, 618-631.

Baluja, S. 1996. Evolution of an Artificial Neural Network Based Autonomous Land Vehicle Controller. *IEEE Transaction on Systems, Man, and Cybernetics – Part B: Cybernetics, vol. 26, no. 3*, 450-463.

Boden, M. A. (Ed.) 1990. *The Philosophy of Artificial Intelligence*. New York: Oxford University Press.

Bornstein, M. H. 1976. Infants' recognition memory for hue. *Developmental Psychology, 12*, 185-191.

Bressler, E. 2005. *Humor and human courtship: Testing predictions from sexual selection theory*. Unpublished doctoral dissertation, McMaster University.

Bressler, E., Martin, R. & Balshine, S. 2006. Production and appreciation of humor as sexually selected traits. *Evolution and Human Behavior, vol. 27, issue 2*, 121-130.

Brodzinsky, D. & Rubien, J. 1976. Humor production as a function of sex of subject, creativity, and cartoon content. *Journal of Consulting and Clinical Psychology, 44*, 597-600.

Buss, D. M. 1994. *The Evolution of Desire: Strategies of Human Mating*. New York: Basic Books.

Buss, D. M. & Barnes, M. 1986. Preferences in human mate selection. *Journal of Personality and Social Psychology, 50*, 559-570.

Carpenter, R. H. S. 2003. *Neurophysiology* (4th ed.). London: Arnold.

Caron, J. E. 2002. From ethology to aesthetics: Evolution as a theoretical paradigm for research on laughter, humor, and other comic phenomena. *International Journal of Humor Research, 15*, 245.

Carroll, J. B. 1993. *Human Cognitive Abilities: A Survey of Factor-analytic Studies*. New York: Cambridge University Press.

Carter, R. 1998. *Mapping The Mind*. London: Weidenfeld & Nicolson.

Carter, R. 2002. *Consciousness*. London: Weidenfeld & Nicolson.

Chapman, A. J. & Foot, H. C. 1976. *Humour and Laughter: Theory, Research, and Applications*. London: Wiley.

Chapman, G., Cleese, J. Gilliam, T., Idle, E., Jones, T., Palin, M. & McCabe, B. 2003. *The Pythons Autobiography*. London: Orion Books.

Chapell, M., Batten, M., Brown, J., Gonzalez, E., Herquet, G., Massar, C. & Pedroche, B. 2002. Frequency of public laughter in relation to sex, age, ethnicity, and social context. *Perceptual and Motor Skills, 95*, 746.

Chomsky, N. 2006. *Language and the Mind* (3rd ed.). Cambridge: Cambridge University Press.

Chugani, H. T., Phelps, M. E., & Mazziotta, J. C. 2002. Positron emission tomography study of human brain functional development. In Johnson, M. H., Munakata, Y. & Gilmore, R. O. (Eds.), *Brain development and cognition: A reader* (2nd ed.). Malden, MA: Blackwell Publishers.

Cliff, D., Husbands, P., Meyer, J. & Wilson, S. W. (Eds.). 1994. *From Animals to Animats III: Proceeding of the Third International Conference on Simulation of Adaptive Behaviour.* Cambridge, Mass.: MIT Press – Bradford Books.

Corballis, M. C. 1999. The gestural origins of language. *American Scientist, 87,* 138–145

Corballis, M. C. 2002. *From Hand to Mouth: The Origin of Language.* Princeton: Princeton University Press.

Darwin, C. 1859/1964. *On the origin of species.* Cambridge, Mass: Harvard University Press.

Darwin, C. 1872/1999. *The Expression of the Emotions in Man and Animals.* London: Fontana Press.

Davila-Ross, M., Menzier, S. & Zimmermann, E. 2008. Rapid facial mimicry in orangutan play. *Biology Letters, 4,* 27-30.

Dawkins, R. 1982/1999. *The extended phenotype: The long reach of the gene.* Oxford: Oxford University Press.

Dawkins, R. 1976/1989. *The selfish gene.* Oxford: Oxford University Press.

Dayan, P. & Abbott, L. F. 2001. *Theoretical Neuroscience: Computational and Mathematical Modelling of Neural Systems.* Cambridge, Mass.: MIT Press.

de Waal, F. B. M. 2008. Putting the Altruism Back into Altruism: The Evolution of Empathy. *Annual Review of Psychology, vol. 59,* 279-300.

Deacon, T. 1997. *The Symbolic Species: The Co-Evolution of Language and the Human Brain.* London: Penguin Books.

Dennett, D. C. 1998. *Brainchildren: Essays on Designing Minds.* London: Penguin Books.

Diamond, A. 2002. Normal development of prefrontal cortex from birth to young adulthood: Cognitive functions, anatomy, and biochemistry. In Stuss, D. T. & Knight, R. T. (Eds.), *Principles of frontal lobe function.* London: Oxford University Press.

Dimberg, U. & Thunberg, M. 1998. Rapid facial reactions to emotional facial expressions. *Scandinavian Journal of Psychology, 39,* 39–45.

Donald, M. 2001. *A Mind So Rare: The Evolution of Human Consciousness.* New York: W.W. Norton & Company.

Dreher, J., Schmidt, P. J., Kohn, P., Furman, D., Rubinow, D. & Berman, K. F. 2007. Menstrual cycle phase modulates reward-related neural function in women. *Proceedings of the National Academy of Sciences of the United States of America (PNAS), 104,* 2465-2470.

Dunbar, R. 1996. *Grooming Gossip and the Evolution of Language.* Cambridge, Mass.: Harvard University Press.

Essock-Vitale, S. & Seyfarth, R. M. 1986. Intelligence and social recognition. In Smuts, B. B. et al (Eds.) *Primate Societies.* Chicago: University of Chicago Press.

Evans, J. St B. T. 2006. Dual System Theories of Cognition: Some Issues. *Cognitive Science Journal, Supplemental Materials, Cognitive Science Conference Proceedings, CogSci 2006:Vancouver, Canada*, 202-207.

Eysenck, H. J. & Eysenck, S. B. G. 1975. *Manual of the Eysenck Personality Questionnaire*. London: Hodder & Stoughton.

Fagan, J. F. 1976. Infants' recognition of invariant features of faces. *Child Development, 47*, 627-638.

Falkenberg, I., Klügel, K., Bartels, M. & Wild, B. 2007. Sense of humor in patients with schizophrenia. *Schizophrenia Research, vol.95, issue 1 - 3*, 259 - 261.

Feingold, A. & Mazzella, R. 1991. Psychometric intelligence and verbal humor ability. *Personality and Individual Differences, 12*, 427-435.

Ferguson, S. M., Schwartz, M. L. & Rayport, M. 1969. Perception of humor in patients with temporal lobe epilepsy: a cartoon test as an indicator of neurpsychological deficit. *Arch Gen Psychiatry, 21*, 363-367.

Fernald, A. & O'Neill, D. K. 1993. Peekaboo across cultures: How mothers and infants play with voices, faces, and expectations. In MacDonald, K. (Ed.), *Parent-child play: Descriptions and implications*. Albany: State University of New York Press.

Gallagher, S. & Zahavi, D. 2007. Phenomenological Approaches to Self-Consciousness. In Zalta, E. N. (Ed.), *The Stanford Encyclopedia of Philosophy*. Stanford University.

Gallese, V., Fadiga, L., Fogassi, L. & Rizzolatti, G. 1996. Action recognition in the premotor cortex. *Brain 119*, 593–609.

Gallup, G. G. 1982. Self-awareness and the emergence of mind in primates. *American Journal of Primatology 2*, 237-248.

Gavanescul, T. 1895. The Altruistic Impulse in Man and Animals. *International Journal of Ethics, vol.5, no.2*, 197-205.

Goldman-Rakic, P. S. 1987. Development of cortical circuitry and cognitive function. *Child Development, 58*, 601-622.

Goldstein, J. H. 1970. Humor appreciation and time to respond. *Psychological Reports, 27*, 445-446.

Goodwin, R. 1990. Sex differences among partner preferences: Are the sexes really very similar? *Sex Roles, 23*, 501-513.

Grammer, K. & Eibl-Eibesfeldt, I. 1990. *The Ritualisation of Laughter*. Bochum: Brockmeyer.

Greenough, W. T., Black, J. E., & Wallace, C. S. 1987. Experience and brain development. *Child Development, 58*, 539-559.

Gregory, R. L. (Ed.) 1987. *The Oxford Companion To The Mind*. New York: Oxford University Press.

Grenader, U. 1996. *Elements of Pattern Theory.* Baltimore: John Hopkins University Press.

Hansen, S. L. 1977. Dating choices of high school students. *The Family Coordinator,* 26, 133-138.

Harris, C. R. 1999. The Mystery of Ticklish Laughter. *American Scientist, 87,* 344-351.

Harris, C. R. & Christenfeld, N. 1997. Humour, tickle and the Darwin-Hecker hypothesis. *Cognition and Emotion, 11,* 103-110.

Harris, C. R. & Christenfeld, N. 1999. Can a machine tickle? *Psychonomic Bulletin & Review, vol. 6, issue 3,* 504-510.

Helmholtz, H. von 1925. *Treatise on physiological optics* (Vol. 3). (Southall, J. P. C. trans.). New York: Dover.

Hewitt, L. E. 1958. Student perceptions of traits desired in themselves as dating and marriage partners. *Marriage and Family Living, Nov.,* 344-349.

Hochberg, J. 1978. *Perception* (2nd ed.). Englewood Cliffs, NJ: Prentice-Hall.

Iacoboni, M., Molnar-Szakacs, I., Gallese, V., Buccino, G., Mazziotta, J. C. et al. 2005. Grasping the intentions of others with one's own mirror neurone system. *PLoS Biology 3(3):* e79.

Iacoboni, M., Woods, R. P., Brass, M., Bekkering, H., Mazziotta, J. C. et al. 1999. Cortical mechanisms of human imitation. *Science 286,* 2526–2528.

Iwase, M., Yamashita, K., Takashi, K., Kajimoto, O., Shimizu, A., Nishikawa, T., Shinosaki, K., Sugita, Y. & Takeda, M. 1999. Diminished facial expression despite the existence of pleasant emotional experience in schizophrenia. *Methods and findings in experimental and clinical pharmacology, vol. 21, issue 3,* 189-94

Johnson, M. H. 1997. *Developmental cognitive neuroscience.* Cambridge, Mass.: Blackwell.

Johnson, M. H., Munakata, Y. & Gilmore, R. O. 2002. *Brain Development and Cognition: A Reader* (2nd ed.). Oxford: Blackwell Publishing.

Jones, S., Martin, R. & Pilbeam, D. (Eds.) 1992. *The Cambridge Encyclopedia of Human Evolution.* Cambridge: Cambridge University Press.

Kaku, M. 1998. *Visions: How Science Will Revolutionize the 21st Century and Beyond.* Oxford: Oxford University Press.

Kandel, E. R. 2006. *In Search of Memory: The Emergence of a New Science of Mind.* New York: W.W. Norton & Company.

Kaufman, S. B., Kozbelt, A., Bromley, M. L. & Miller, G. F. 2007. The role of creativity and humor in mate selection. In Geher, G. & Miller, G. (Eds.), *Mating intelligence: Sex, relationships, and the mind's reproductive system.* Mahwah: Erlbaum.

Keysers, C., Kohler, E., Umilta, M. A., Nanetti, L., Fogassi, L., et al. 2003. Audiovisual mirror neurons and action recognition. *Experimental Brain Research* 153, 628–636.

Kimbrough Oller, D. & Griebel, U. (Eds.) 2004. *Evolution of Communication Systems: A Comparative Approach.* Cambridge, Mass.: MIT Press.

Köhler, G. & Ruch, W. 1996. Sources of variance in current sense of humor inventories: How much substance, how much method variance? *Humor: The International Journal of Humor Research, 9,* 363-397.

Koestler, A. 1964. *The act of creation.* London: Arkana/Penguin. Reprint 1989.

Kolb, K. (Ed.) 1990. Humor. In Center for Early Education and Development, University of Minnesota *Early Report vol.18, no.1.*

Kris, E. 1939. Des Lachen Als Mimischer Vorgang: (Laughter as Mimicry.) *Int. Ztschr. f. Psa. u. Imago, XXIV,* 146–168.

Lecoeuche, R., Catinaud, O. & Gréboval-Barry, C. 1996. Competence in Human Beings and Knowledge-based Systems. *Proceedings of Tenth Knowledge Acquisition for Knowledge-Based Systems Workshop.*

Legrand, D. 2007. Pre-Reflective Self-Consciousness: On Being Bodily in the World. *Janus Head, 9(2),* 493-519.

Lenski, G. & Lenski, J. 1987. *Human Societies: An Introduction to Macrosociology* (5th ed.). Singapore: McGraw-Hill Book Company.

Lieberman, P. 1998. *Eve Spoke: Human Language and Human Evolution.* London: Picador.

Luck, S. J. & Vogel, E. K. 1997. The capacity of visual working memory for features and conjunctions. *Nature, 390,* 279-281.

Mareschal, D. & Johnson, M. H. 2003. The "what" and "where" of object representations in infancy. *Cognition, 88,* 259-276.

Margolis, H. 1987. *Patterns, Thinking, and Cognition: A Theory of Judgement.* Chicago: University of Chicago Press.

Masten, A.S. 1986. Humor and competence in school-aged children. *Child Development, 57,* 461-473.

Matari , M. J. 1994, Reward Functions for Accelerated Learning. In Cohen, W. W., & Hirsh, H. (Eds.), *Machine Learning: Proceedings of the Eleventh International Conference.* San Francisco: Morgan Kaufmann Publishers.

Matthiessen, C. M. I. M. 2000. The evolution of language: A systemic functional exploration of phylogenetic phases. *3rd Conference of The Evolution of Language: Abstracts,* April 3rd – 6th.

Maynard Smith, J. 1975/1993. *The Theory of Evolution.* Cambridge: Canto – Cambridge University Press.

McCrone, J. 1991. *The Ape That Spoke: Language and the Evolution of the Human Mind.* New York: William Morrow.

McGhee, P. E. 1979. *Humor: Its Origin and Development.* San Francisco: Freeman.

McGhee, P. E. 2002. *Understanding and Promoting the Development of Children's Humor.* Dubuque: Kendall/Hunt.

McLeod, P., Plunkett, K. & Rolls, E. T. 1998. *Introduction to Connectionist Modelling of Cognitive Processes.* New York: Oxford University Press.

Meadows, S. 2006. *The Child as Thinker: The Development and Acquisition of Cognition in Childhood* (2nd ed.). Hove: Routledge.

Meltzoff, A. N. & Moore, M. K. 1977. Imitation of facial and manual gestures by human neonates. *Science, 198,* 75-78.

Michaud, F. & Matari , M. J. 1997 Behavior Evaluation and Learning from an Internal Point of View. *Proceedings, FLAIRS-97,* Daytona, Florida.

Miller, D., Harrub, B. & Thompson, B. 2002. The Origin of Language and Communication. *Apologetics Press: Reason & Revelation, 22(8),* 57-63.

Mithen, S. 1996. *The Prehistory of the Mind.* London: Thames and Hudson.

Mithen, S. 2002. Human evolution and the cognitive basis of science. In Carruthers, P., Stich, S. & Siegal, M. (Eds.) *The Cognitive Basis of Science.* Cambridge: Cambridge University Press.

Mondada, F. & Floreano, D. 1995. Evolution of neural control structures: some experiments on mobile robots. *Robotics and Autonomous Systems, 16,* 183-195.

Montague, D. P. F. & Walker-Andrews, A. S. 2001. Peekaboo: A New Look at Infants' Perception of Emotion Expressions. *Developmental Psychology, vol. 37, no. 6,* 826-838.

Nairne, J. S. 2006. *Psychology: The Adaptive Mind* (4th ed.). Belmont: Thomson Wadsworth.

Nelson, C. A. 1987. The recognition of facial expressions in the first two years of life: Mechanisms of development. *Child Development, 58,* 889-909

Nelson, C. A. 1995. The ontogeny of human memory: A cognitive neuroscience perspective. *Developmental Psychology, 31,* 723-738.

Newcombe, N., Huttenlocher, J. & Learmonth, A. 1999. Infants' coding of location in continuous space. *Infant Behavior & Development, 22,* 483-510.

Newell, A. & Simon, H. A. 1972. *Human Problem Solving.* Prentice-Hall.

Oakes, L. M. & Bauer, P. J. 2007. *Short- and Long-Term Memory in Infancy and Early Childhood.* Oxford: Oxford University Press.

Otto, B. K. 2001. *Fools Are Everywhere.* Chicago: University of Chicago Press.

Owens, H. M., & Hogan, J. D. 1983. Development of humor in children: Roles of incongruity, resolution, and operational thinking. *Psychological Reports, 53,* 477-478.

Parrott, W. G. & Gleitman, H. 1989. Infant's expectations in play: The joy of peek-a-boo. *Cognition and Emotion, vol. 3,* 291-311.

Parvizi, J., Anderson, S. W., Martin, C. O., Damasio, H. & Damasio, A. R. 2001. Pathological laughter and crying: A link to the cerebellum. *Brain, 124,* 1708-1719.

Pert, C. B. 1999. *Molecules of Emotion: Why You Feel The Way You Feel.* London: Pocket Books.

Pertschuk, M. & Trisdorfer, A. 1994. Men's Bodies: The Survey. *Psychology Today, Nov/Dec, article id: 1407.*

Pien, D. & Rothbart, M. K. 1980. Incongruity humour, play, and self-regulation of arousal in young children. In McGhee, P. E. & Chapman, A. J. (Eds.) *Children's Humor.* Chichester.

Pinker, S. 1994. *The Language Instinct.* New York: William Morrow and Company.

Pinker, S. 1999. *How the Mind Works.* London: Penguin Books.

Pinker, S. 2003. *The Blank Slate.* London: Penguin Books.

Pinker, S. & Bloom, P. & commentators. 1990. Natural Language and Natural Selection. *Behavioral and Brain Sciences, 13,* 707-784.

Plotnik, J. M., de Waal, F. B. M. & Reiss, D. 2006. Self-recognition in an Asian Elephant. *PNAS, vol. 103, no. 45,* 17053-17057.

Poirier, F. E., Bellisari, A. & Haines, L. 1977. Functions of Primate Play Behavior. In Smith, E. O. (Ed.) *Social Play in Primates.* New York: Academic Press Inc.

Provine, R. R. 1992. Contagious Laughter: Laughter is sufficient stimulus for laughs and smiles. *Bulletin of the Psychonomic Society, 30,* 1-4.

Provine, R. R. 1993. Laughter punctuates speech: Linguistic, social, and gender contexts of laughter. *Ethology, 95,* 291-298.

Provine, R. R. 1996. Laughter. *American Scientist, 84,* 38-45.

Provine, R. R. 2000. *Laughter: A Scientific Investigation.* London: Faber and Faber.

Provine, R. R. & Fischer, K. R. 1989. Laughing, Smiling, and talking: Relation to sleeping and social context in humans. *Ethology, 83,* 295-305.

Provine, R. R. & Yong, Y. L. 1991. Laughter: A stereotyped human vocalization. *Ethology, 89,* 115-124.

Quinn, P. C. 1994. The categorization of above and below spatial relations by young infants. *Child Development, 65,* 58-69.

Reddy, V., Williams, E. & Vaughan, A. 2002. Sharing humour and laughter in autism and Down's syndrome. *British Journal of Psychology, vol. 93, no. 2,* 219-242

Regan, P. C. & Joshi, A. 2003. Ideal partner preferences among adolescents. *Social Behavior and Personality, 31,* 13-20.

Reiss A. L., Azim, E., Mobbs, D., Jo, B. & Menon, V. 2005. Sex differences in brain activation elicited by humor. *PNAS, 102:45,* 16496-501

Reynolds, P. C. 2002. Pretending Primates: Play and Simulation in the Evolution of Primate Societies. In Mitchell, R. W. (Ed.) *Pretending and Imagination in Animals and Children.* Cambridge: Cambridge University Press.

Rizzolatti, G., Fadiga, L., Gallese, V. & Fogassi, L. 1996. Premotor cortex and the recognition of motor actions. *Cognitive Brain Research 3*, 131–141

Rochat, P., Querido J. G. & Striano, T. 1999. Emerging sensitivity to the timing and structure of protoconversation in early infancy. *Developmental Psychology, vol. 35*, 950-957.

Roeckelein, J. E. 2002. *The Psychology of Humor: A Reference Guide and Annotated Bibliography.* Westport, CT: Greenwood Press.

Rose, S. A., Gottfried, A. W., Mello-Carmina, P. & Bridger, W. H. 1982. Familiarity and novelty preferences in infant recognition memory: Implications for information processing. *Developmental Psychology, 18*, 704-713.

Ross-Sheehy, S., Oakes, L. M. & Luck, S. J. 2003. The Development of Visual Short-Term Memory Capacity in Infants. *Child Development, vol. 74, issue 6*, 1807-1822.

Rothbart, M. K. 1976. Incongruity, problem-solving and laughter. In Chapman, A. J. & Foot, H. C. (Eds.) *Humour and Laughter: theory, research and applications.* Chichester.

Rucas, S. L., Gurven, M., Kaplan, H., Winking, J., Gangestad, S. & Crespo, M. 2006. Female intrasexual competition and reputational effects on attractiveness among the Tsimane of Bolivia. *Evolution and Human Behavior, 27*, 40-52.

Saczawa, M. 2005. The Types and Duration of Play in a Solitary Species (Pongo pygmacus) versus a Social Species (Mandrillus leucophaeus). *Oxford Journal of Anthropology, 1.*

Savage-Rumbaugh, S. & Lewin, R. 1994. Ape at the brink. *Discover 15(9)*, 90-96,98

Sheehy-Skeffington, A. 1977. The measurement of humor appreciation. In Chapman, A. J. & Foot, H. C. (Eds.), *It's a Funny Thing, Humour.* Oxford: Pergamon Press.

Slater, A. & Lewis, M. (Eds.) 2007. *Introduction to Infant Development* (2nd ed.). Oxford: Oxford University Press.

Smith, E. E. & Jonides, J. 1997. Working memory: A view from neuroimaging. *Cognitive Psychology, 33*, 5-42.

Smith, J. E., Waldorf, V. A. & Trembath, D. L. 1990. "Single white male looking for thin, very attractive...," *Sex Roles, 23*, 675-685.

Smock, T. K. 1999. Physiological Psychology: *A Neuroscience Approach.* New Jersey: Prentice Hall.

Spelke, E. S. 1990. Principles of Object Perception. *Cognitive Science, 14*, 29-56.

Spitz, R. A. & Wolf, K. M. 1946. The smiling response: A contribution to the ontogenesis of social relations. *Genetic Psychology Monographs, vol. 34*, 57-125.

Sprecher, S., & Regan, P. C. 2000. Liking some things (in some people) more than others: Partner preferences in romantic relationships and friendships. *Journal of Social and Personal Relationships, 19*, 463-481.

Sroufe, L. A. & Piccard Wunsch, J. 1972. The Development of Laughter in the First Year of Life. *Child Development, vol. 43, no. 4*, 1326-1344.

Sroufe, L. A. & Waters, E. 1976. The ontogenesis of smiling and laughter: A perspective on the organization of development in infancy. *Psychological Review, vol. 83*, 173-189.

Stainton, R. J. (Ed.) 2006. *Contemporary Debates in Cognitive Science.* Oxford: Blackwell Publishing.

Storey, R. 2002. Humor and sexual selection. *Human Nature, 14*, 319-336.

Tallis, R. 2008. *The Kingdom of Infinite Space: A Fantastical Journey Around Your Head.* London: Atlantic Books.

Tateno, A., Jorge, R. E. & Robinson, R. G. 2004. Pathological Laughing and Crying Following Traumatic Brain Injury. *The Journal of Neuropsychiatry and Clinical Neurosciences, 16*, 426-434.

Todosijevic, B., Snezana, L. & Arancic, A. 2003. Mate selection criteria: A trait desirability assessment study of sex differences in Serbia. *Evolutionary Psychology, 1*, 116-126.

Tomasello, M. 1999. *The Cultural Origins of Human Cognition.* Cambridge, Mass.: Harvard University Press.

Toro-Morn, M. & Sprecher, S. 2003. A cross-cultural comparison of mate preferences among University students; The United States versus the People's Republic of China (PRC). *Journal of Comparative Family Studies, 34*, 151-170.

Umilta, M.A., Kohler, E., Gallese, V., Fogassi, L., Fadiga, L., et al. 2001. I know what you are doing. A neurophysiological study. *Neuron 31*, 155–165.

van Hooff, J. A. R. A. M. & Preuschoft, S. 2003. Laughter and smiling: the intertwining of nature and culture. In de Waal, F. B. M. & Tyack, P. L. (Eds.) *Animal social complexity: intelligence, culture, and individualized societies.* Cambridge, Mass.: Harvard University Press.

Walsh Hokenson, J. 2006. *The Idea of Comedy: History, Theory, Critique.* Cranbury: Fairleigh Dickinson University Press.

Wild, B., Rodden, F. A., Grodd, W. & Ruch, W. 2003. Neural correlates of laughter and humour. *Brain, 126*, 2121-2138.

Wilson, E. O. 1975/2000. *Sociobiology: The New Synthesis.* Cambridge, Mass.: Belknap Press of Harvard University Press.

Wilson, R. A. & Keil, F. C. 1999. *The MIT Encyclopedia of the Cognitive Sciences.* Cambridge, Mass.: MIT Press.

Wyer, R. S. & Collins, J. E. 1992. A theory of humor elicitation. *Psychological Review, vol. 99(4)*, 663-688.

Yamauchi, B. & Beer, R. D. 1994. Sequential behavior and learning in evolved dynamical neural networks. *Adaptive Behavior 2 (3)*, 219-246.

Zillmann, D. 1983. Disparagement humor. In McGhee, P. E. & Goldstein, J. H. (Eds.) *Handbook of Humor Research*. New York: Springer-Verlag.

Zimmer, C. 2001. *Evolution*. New York: HarperCollins.

Index